THE
HANDSTANDING
YOGI

THE HOWS, WHYS & WTFS
OF BEING UPSIDEDOWN

ASH BOND &
GABRIELLE PARKER

ILLUSTRATIONS BY SIMONSI

Dear Anni,

How do I express how
mind-blowingly amazing you
are ...

In gratitude,
all g gatsby
:) xxx.

This book is written as a guide to help you on your individual journey upside down. It is not meant as a replacement for a good teacher.

Especially if you are new to inversions or are on a healing journey, please check with a medical professional as to your fitness and suitability for exercise.

Handstands are magical things. Please use this magic wisely with no other intention than to increase your own unique brand of awesome.

You are awesome.

In gratitude,

Matador
9 Priory Business Park,
Wistow Road, Kibworth Beauchamp,
Leicestershire. LE8 0RX
Tel: 0116 279 2299
Email: books@troubador.co.uk
Web: www.troubador.co.uk/matador
Twitter: @matadorbooks

ISBN 9781788039529

British Library Cataloguing in Publication Data.
A catalogue record for this book is available from the British Library.

Printed by CPI Ltd, Croyden, UK
Typeset in 12pt Bembo by Troubador Publishing Ltd, Leicester, UK

Matador is an imprint of Troubador Publishing Ltd

To our parents and housemates who let us use their kitchen tables to write this book.

And to our students, who will always be our best teachers.

"Why do you want to climb Mount Everest?"

"...Because it's there."

— George Mallory in
Climbing Mount Everest is work for Supermen,
The New York Times, 1923

Contents

The Handstander: Gabby. 4'11". Professional acrobat and handstand teacher. Gabby is a terrible yoga student, although she tries.

The Yogi: Ash. 5'2". Yoga teacher and writer. Ash can not really handstand, please don't ask her to.

Prologue

"Don't cheat, I see everything."

I was *squeezing* everything. I looked at myself—upside down in the studio mirror, the person staring back at me was red-faced and noticeably twitching. Oh my god, that person also looked like she was crying.

Calm down, you absolute moron. I tried to blink the tears away, the tears which were mercifully at least indistinguishable from the sweat rushing from my toes all the way to my sticky fingertips.

I was tired, I was embarrassed and I was 100% sure I had made the wrong decision in coming here. I mean, what was *I* doing in a handstand class?

This was all coupled with the increasingly obvious truth that I had made very bad handstand clothing choices — my voluminous tee that I had attempted to stuff into my running leggings had managed to wriggle free almost immediately and fallen to expose my trusty sports bra that was working, and failing, to stop my boobs escaping — defeated by gravity. This is how people die upside down, I thought: ineffectual sporting attire. A few haggard breaths later and I crumpled gracelessly to the ground.

I had arrived that rainy Bristol evening to local teacher Gabrielle Parker's popular and infamously humbling handstand class. An hour before I'd been supervising Homework Club, handing out pencils, tackling algebra equations and policing the photocopier ("don't even think about printing that in colour") but in the jog from school to studio I had transformed — tired yet confident teacher was now delicate and bricking it student.

Actually I had arrived late, and my first interaction with Gabby 'Gabbatron' Parker was her asking me politely, yet firmly, to do push-ups as recompense. I stared at her. She stared back — as if to say "glaring at me is all well and good but it won't make you better at handstands. You know what will make you better at handstands? Push-ups." I decided absolutely in that moment that her, me and most certainly handstands were not going to get on.

It was now 6 months later and I was only just beginning to forgive her.

"Love is a temporary madness, it erupts like volcanoes and then subsides. And when it subsides, you have to make a decision. You have to work out whether your roots have so entwined together that it is inconceivable that you should ever part. Because this is what love is."

— Louis de Bernières, *Captain Corelli's Mandolin*

"So seriously, tell me, what is the big deal with handstands in yoga?" Gabby still hadn't looked up from her phone where she was flicking quizzically through sunset-filtered photographs as if they were profiles on a Tinder account. Would I want to date this handstand? Swipe right for yes, left for no.

I shrugged, suddenly intently interested in my latte as I swirled it with a spoon. Yeah, that's alright for you to say, I thought enviously. You can *do* a handstand. Only people who can actually *do* handstands are allowed to say they're not a 'big deal'.

We'd met in Bristol's rapidly gentrifying hipster hub of Stokes Croft. Our new favourite café was squeezed between a pop-up bakery and a place to buy artist prints and hand-painted cushion covers. It was our favourite because it sold avocados, eggs and coffee — all of our favourite things — in all possible permutations. The café's clientele consisted predominantly of squads of students and the self-employed, the ranks of which Gabby and I joined gleefully. Occasionally, only very occasionally, a customer would try and charge a non-Apple product under one of the large rustic tables and they would be stared at, the onlooker confused as to why they would make their life so much harder than it actually had to be.

"No, really," ignoring the eye-rolling, Gabby waved her (Apple) phone at me: an Instagram picture of an upside down Beach Yoga Girl flashed before my face. "It's like if you have a good handstand, it makes you some kind of Yoga *god*. I mean, is it really that impressive?"

Well yes, I thought, yes it is.

Gabby tapped the screen pointedly. "You know what is impressive—look at those insane hamstrings, so freakin' flexi!"

I felt cornered. Myself and my yoga compadres were getting called out and I did not have an answer. Gabby was right of course — posters for handstand workshops cover the walls of studios, quietly yet earnestly multiplying and pushing the 'yinner' offerings out to the fringes, like big fat papery acro-cuckoos.

For some, these acrobatics represent a shallow temptation to students stuck in the lower limbs of the yoga hierarchy, drawing them with promises of extreme strength, flexibility and fame. For others, a handstand is a celebration of freedom, a tantalising physical goal that deserves its place at the yoga table due mainly to the disciplined practice it takes to achieve.

It is however a truth that within this fast-growing yoga biz 'the handstand' is held up as something of a pot of gold, an elusive reward at the end of the yoga asana rainbow. Those who have achieved it are revered as epic heroes, returning from a long and treacherous voyage and are showered with appreciative nods, Instagram likes, sponsorship deals and guest spots at festivals.

"Did you see his handstand? He's so hot"

— Lululemon, *Sh*t That Yogis Say*

For me, handstands represented a tangible, potentially achievable prize that guiltily teased at my Type A desire to accomplish; the part of me that my yoga had quietly sidelined. A handstand was something outside of my regular practice that I could steadily work away on, strive and train for. Or at least it would have been, if I had actually trained for it.

So I didn't train handstands, but I did daydream about them. I would imagine myself jauntily rocking out a nifty balance in the middle of a festival field surrounded suddenly by a hushed and awed audience.

'Oh, what? You saw that? I've only been training 10 hours a week for a year to do that. No biggie'.

I grabbed her phone, still displaying the hamstringily-gifted girl and read the post attached. According to the text beneath the photo, the pose itself is unimportant — it's in the journey, that's where the real learning happens. I read it aloud.

Gabby arched a quizzical eyebrow. She did not look convinced.

I looked again. Rachel Brathan and her tanned handstand had fifteen thousand Instagram likes. No denying it, yoga — a practice once so focused on the stillness of the seated posture — had entered into an inversion affair that was showing no signs of simmering down. We, amateur acrobats and social media surfers alike, were infatuated.

v

It was a heated affair for sure, but would it last? When the pretty blossoms fell away would yoga and acrobatics still have their roots intertwined, hugging lovingly to each other, or was it a fleeting flirtation — yoga having found itself temporarily seduced by the glamour of the upside down?

"Is it just that it's cool?" I nodded, handstands are cool.

"Or is it the strength?" Uh huh, the strength too.

"Is it that there aren't that many people who can do it in yoga?"

Er...

She wanted to know why, I wanted to know how. Two more years and a few thousand lattes later, we wrote this book.

PART
I

THE FOUNDATIONS

*If I had two wishes, I know what t
hey would be. I'd wish for Roots
to cling to, and Wings to set me free.*

- Denis Waitley

The Foundations

1. Introduction

This is a book for those who…

- Think they will never be able to do a handstand
- Don't know if they even *want* to do a handstand
- Know that they want to do a handstand but also know that they are in need of some serious guidance and/or fairy dust
- Do yoga a little
- Do yoga a lot

This is me, all of the above is me. The casually stated fact of 'oh, I don't really do handstands' has been part of my yoga teaching spiel for a while now. There were even a few years when the idea that a particularly zealous student might suddenly stand up and yell 'what do you mean you *can't* do a handstand?' was the subject of more than one Lycra-clad nightmare.

It's not that I don't like them, I mean if 'handstands' were a person I wouldn't ignore them on the street — I would nod and smile, maybe wave like you would to a friend of a friend, I just wouldn't invite them out for cocktails is all. And then I met handstand teacher Gabby and handstands actually *did* become a person and the 'oh I don't really do handstands' became less of a fact and, well, more of an excuse.

But at one point, I *did* do handstands, we all did. Before the iGeneration, we were all those kids in the playground throwing ourselves upside down with no fear of falling, no worries that our pinafores would fall over our heads or our hands would get muddy; no hang-ups of looking silly, of looking like we were trying too hard or fear of somebody posting a cringe-worthy photograph of us on Facebook. We've all been there once, and sometimes in those brief moments of tentative balance and even in those more familiar moments of crashing to the ground, we get there again.

If you have picked up (or perhaps successfully Googled) *The Handstanding Yogi: The Hows, Whys and WTFs of Being Upside Down* it may be that you too are in the throes of learning to invert or perhaps you are just considering dipping your toes — cautiously poised at the edge of the handstanding pool. You are wise to be wary; the journey to a safe and stable handstand is paved with elation, frustration and all that lives in between (or so I hear).

My own journey to answering Gabby's seemingly simple question of 'what is the big deal with handstands?' would take me to Bali, via San Francisco, Sweden and Montréal. In understanding the power of turning your world on its head and onto your hands I would discover mind-bogglingly beautiful art made by the humblest of circus souls, rockstar yogis baring all to teach people a lesson in loving themselves, yoga warriors who combat addictions with the high of being upside down and teachers in whose hands handstands are fonts of strength for those who need it most. I would see that handstands have made careers, broken egos, crippled bodies, given people roots and even gifted some of the luckier ones wings.

My journey would make me want to dust off my pinafore and join the ranks of the upside down, but for now: engage your glutes; pull your lower ribs in; take your arms up and shoulders to your ears.

Are you sitting uncomfortably? Then we shall begin...

2. *The Pillars of Handstand*

Gabby, pain in my squat-shy butt that she is, is also a petite powerhouse of acrobatic know-how. Almost everything you want to know about how to get upside down safely is stuffed into that brain of hers.

In this book we have taken all of this handstanding info and broken it down into the most basic skills that make up the foundations of safe and efficient inversion training; we have called these the 'pillars of handstand'.

- Specific Strength
- Endurance
- Alignment
- Consistency
- Shape
- Mobility and Flexibility
- Balance

You can of course attain a handstand without building up a strong acrobatic foundation — many people do. Gabby teaches these foundations for handstand because they build efficiency, consistency and lay a safe, stable base on which to develop your skills. These handstand foundations will take different people varying amounts of time to achieve for reasons varying from body type and previous experience to basic mindset and willingness to commit to training. For some it will take just a few months, for others it will take a year or more. Once you have attained these foundations however, suddenly the more advanced shapes seem that much more within your grasp. Meet Nicolas Montes De Oca, or 'Nico'. Nico is an international circus performer and professional handbalance teacher, instructing students worldwide. He is also the author of the 'tuck against the wall' drill that you will learn to love and fear all at the same time (p72).

The first circus school that Nico went to he didn't go as a handstander, he went as a juggler. Only later, obsessed with the idea of becoming a handbalancer, he asked to switch disciplines. He was told that he couldn't specialise in handbalance.

Well, all teachers get things wrong sometimes and all teachers were once students and in his fight to get upside down Nico had first to learn his foundations. He snapped them up defiantly fast; he had the mobility, the athletic build, the endurance — but that wasn't his most impressive feat. On mastering all of these foundational elements he achieved a one-armed handstand in just under four months. Gabby's initial response to this information was (not atypically) "Fuck off. Four months to a one-arm?" She did however absolutely believe him — his line was just that good that when it was time for him to increase his skill level all of the jigsaw pieces were already there, all of the building blocks. Of course Nico is not your average student, and your average student also does not have the fortune to train with infamously hardcore Chinese circus instructors, as Nico did. To build a strong foundation takes time and work, and it is a long and arduous process that is tempting to skip. If you do decide to skip these foundations you run the risky gauntlet of:

a) your handstand taking a much longer time to build
b) injury through not preparing the body appropriately
c) the inability to build upon your handstand

You have been warned.

Specific Strength

What is it?

Building and learning to engage (and disengage) relevant and particular muscles (and muscle groups) that specifically relate to efficient and correct technique within handbalance.

Why do we train it?

The handstand journey starts with this integral step. The base of handstand is building specific strength whether on the floor or in the air. We break it down, analyse and isolate limiting or weak factors and repeat relevant conditioning techniques to prepare the body to stand on our hands with ease and efficiency, sans injury.

Endurance

What is it?

The ability to endure a length of time within handstand without failure from muscles or mind.

Why do we train it?

Without endurance we lose our technique quickly, we are then limiting the speed of our journey to progress in any other area of handbalance.

Alignment

What is it?

The ability to understand and achieve a straight line in handstand.

Why do we train it?

We train alignment to end body habits such as an arched 'banana' back, closed shoulders, or flared ribs, enabling us to build on a safe, solid structure. We also learn how to 'stack weight' within the handstand by focusing on good alignment. With good alignment comes the second part of the handstand journey of learning to balance; without good alignment, correct and safe balance technique will be inconsistent and lengthy. A strong understanding and practice of correct handstand alignment creates options for style, creativity and movement in an inverted position such as body/leg isolations and progressions to harder or more technical shapes, skills and figures such as the one-arm handstand.

Consistency

What is it?

The process of building muscle memory into the body despite your emotional or mental status or feeling. The creation of an individualised program, regularity and repetition within your training routine.

Why do we train it?

Consistency is a hugely important element of handstand practice. In most acrobatic based skills or disciplines we want to train muscle memory. After around 300 repetitions of the same correct exercise, we can stop using our brains and let our body do the practice. This builds an enjoyable way to practise because we're not having to have an 'on form' mental state for our body to be able to perform a difficult task. Consistency training is also a great way of training to eliminate habits quickly. For example learning to kick to handstand, learning to stack the hips over the shoulders involves many repetitions of the same action so that we eventually learn to consistently kick to handstand with fluidity, ease and technique. With consistency, we are able to effectively speed up the process of developing a good handstand and further learning new handstand skills.

Shape

What is it?

From the nuances of handstand (i.e. getting the perfect straight line) to learning body isolations and creating basic shapes such as tuck, straddle, pike; also includes movement within the handstand (i.e. leg isolations, transfers and transitions into shapes, figures or one-arms.)

Why do we train it?

Correct technique in basic shapes on two arms will lead to progression for the same shapes in one-arm or moving between shapes and positions, having the ability to build creativity, movement, style, fluidity with a good understanding and practice of the foundational shapes within handstand.

Balance

What is it?

Balance is the part that allows us to hold the handstand.

Why do we train it?

Think about balancing in handstand as the same as standing on the feet; your toes will rescue you from falling over or having to take a step. It is the same upside down: you want to use your fingers to balance the handstand.

While often the pillar that students want to focus on the most, balance is usually the shortest part of the journey and is last in this list for a reason.

You can imagine the journey in two parts, the first part being about building that specific strength and alignment, learning to stack weight and make the right shape with the body. Then the second is balance. Learning to balance before having correct alignment will make the journey ultimately longer.

If you skip the other pillars you are likely to end up with what Gabby affectionately refers to as 'the fish handstand'. This is a handstand that is balanced from the body, rather than being controlled by the hands and fingers.

Mobility/Flexibility

What is it?

Mobility allows our bodies to functionally move and play. It allows us to access varied positions with our bodies. Flexibility is such a vast topic it deserves a whole other book (watch this space).

Why do we train it?

Specific flexibility or mobility makes it more accessible to perform or practise at a higher level within our desired discipline or chosen specific move/position.

Finding your perfect handstand is like baking the perfect cake: as a professional you know what ingredients you need and how much to use of each. You don't need to be worried too much about the results. It just takes a lot of half-baked culinary disasters to get there.

All of us have our strengths and our challenges. To help us understand how we can use these pillars to shape our handstand training we have included case studies after each chapter where Gabby has given each student a rating out of 5 for each pillar. She has then listed exercises that she would give that student to help target their areas of challenge. A full list of exercises can be found in the middle of this book (p45), each of these exercises is also connected to one or more of these foundational skills.

3. *The Acrobatic Handstand*

The 'acrobatic' or 'circus' handstand as it is now differs quite noticeably (once you know what to look for) from the more traditional 'yoga' handstand.

While it differs hugely depending on what style of yoga you practise, we yogis are very used to dragging the scapula down, keeping the chest open and the shoulders back. This is fabulous for our posture but if we're doing this as a daily practice it does influence muscle group strength, development and memory when trying to find a handstand position.

In handstand, this taking the scapula down often leads to a yoga body having what in acrobatic terms would be called 'closed' shoulders. This shape lends itself to a handstand form where the chest is out, the back is slightly arched and the feet end up drifting over the shoulders and wrists to compensate. If done regularly without understanding of how to properly activate, utilise and strengthen the serratus muscle the rotator cuff muscles are likely to suffer.

The photograph in **BKS** Iyengar's *Light on Yoga* of him in
Adho Mukha Vrksasana (translated as 'downward facing tree
pose') is the shape of an almost perfectly shaped letter 'J',
with his legs pointed straight up to the sky and his chest
curving towards the ground.

This 'J' shape is working with the natural curve, it is
working with the body. It is a beautiful handstand shape
found in nature — if you ever see a chimpanzee
handstand, and you should (it's adorable), you will see the
naturally curved 'banana' back.

A pencil straight 'acrobatic' line is not something we
expect to see in nature, it is something we see in circus — a
place of fantasy, an art form where artists have worked
rigorously to mould their bodies into these hypnotic, alien
shapes. So while yoga follows the natural lines, the
acrobatic form works against the natural curve of the body
to create a strong enough platform from which new and
interesting artistic shapes can be created.

Also in acrobatics, physics has won out.

Adho Mukha Vrksasana, the yoga handstand has evolved with
a different purpose in mind from the circus handstand and
as a consequence the shape is different, just as the circus
handstand shape differs just a little from that of a
gymnastic handstand. These subtly different shapes are
clustered under the umbrella of 'handstand' but have
slightly different structures depending on what the
practitioner is doing with them — tumbling, flying,
handbalancing etc.

Yoga loves playing with the idea of perception, yogis daily
navigating their way through a mindful practice trying to

become increasingly conscious of the 'narrow chinks' through which we view things. In this vein, none of these poses are more or less correct than any of the others — the confusion happens when we ask one pose to do the job of another. For example, if a yogi spends as much time upside down as say a handbalancer in a pose without the proper preparation, the pressure on certain parts of the body can become too much.

The circus handstand, in its current aligned form, has been developed so as to avoid injury and to create a route for progression for those that perform with it over years of structural analysis. The Chinese circus found that they could contort in their handstands, making art that way, but it was the Russians who applied the analytical tools and upon finding the perfect line gave handbalance another jump in evolution.

Science and aesthetics have combined to create the 'handstand stack' or as Gabby calls it 'the building blocks'.

4. The Building Block Conversation

When discussing handstand alignment Gabby often talks in reference to building blocks — quite literally the children's building blocks with numbers and letters printed on them. These building blocks represent structure and weakness in structure.

In a perfectly aligned handstand the building blocks would be stacked neatly on top of one another so that if we added another force on top, say gravity, the building blocks are unlikely to fall over. If you have rushed your build however and your ABC blocks are a little on the wonky side, your shoulders a little closed off say or your back a little banana-y, then anything — even a light breeze — is likely to knock you off your game.

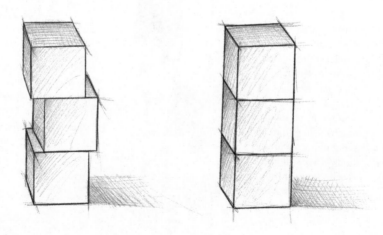

5. *How to Build a Handstand*
What are my key cues?
Why does this help my handstand?

1. Push the floor away and superglue the ears to the shoulders
Why? We want to focus on lengthening the body in handstand position. The shoulders want to be on top of the wrists and hips on top of the shoulders; this means we can 'stack weight' properly. Keeping the ears close to the shoulders will also prevent them from moving into either a 'closed' or 'open' position and prevent a tense neck.

2. Imagine screwing a lightbulb in from the shoulders (right hand clockwise, left hand anticlockwise)
Why? To create external rotation of the shoulder which creates "torque" and stability within the shoulder joint. It also helps us with shoulder protraction and serratus anterior engagement.

3. Imagine having a corset around the chest.
Why? This keeps the ribs down. Contraction of your anterior core muscles prevent the ribs from flaring. It also prevents the loss of intra-abdominal

4. Squeeze the bum
Why? Activating the gluteal muscles helps create a straight line from the hands to the toes.

6. The Anatomy of Handstand
What is happening anatomically in my handstand shape?

What are the primary muscles involved?

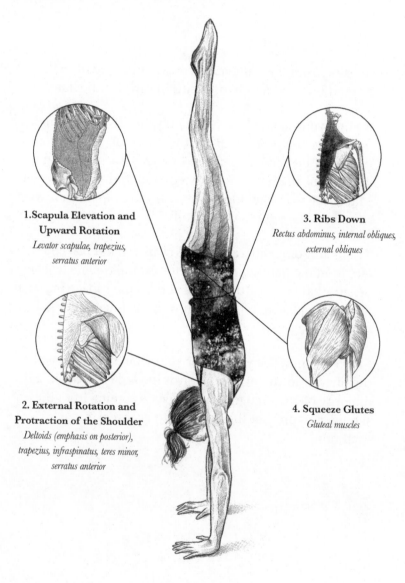

1.Scapula Elevation and Upward Rotation
Levator scapulae, trapezius, serratus anterior

3. Ribs Down
Rectus abdominus, internal obliques, external obliques

2. External Rotation and Protraction of the Shoulder
Deltoids (emphasis on posterior), trapezius, infraspinatus, teres minor, serratus anterior

4. Squeeze Glutes
Gluteal muscles

.7. *Hand Placement*

Starting from the foundations means building from the ground up — and in handstands this means the hands.

To find your hand placement pop yourself into a four-point kneeling position. Place the index finger down on to the floor, this is the finger that should be facing forwards. The rest of the fingers get placed around the index finger. Make sure your shoulders are stacked on top of your wrists so you have weight in your hands.

There are some different ways in which hand placement is taught in the handstand world, for example some teachers believe that cupping the hands and keeping space between the floor and front of the palm with the fingers closed is safer for the wrists.

Often you may see yourself or your training buddy with the fingers slowly turning inwards toward each other. The majority of the time this movement is coming from the shoulder, to prevent this we need to access external rotation.

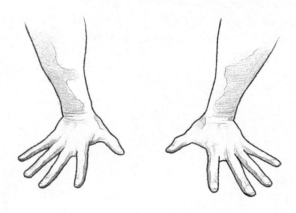

Our preferred placement
External rotation: index finger facing forwards

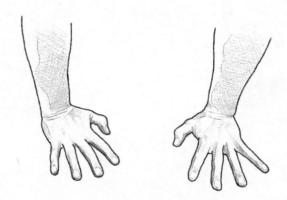

Internal rotation: index fingers facing towards each other

8. Scapula Elevation

These exercises are for the anatomically geeky amongst you, the ones who shamelessly check out the fine musculature of the interior tibialis on the cyclist next to you. You know who you are, Will.

Equipment needed: Foam roller, mirror (optional)

Standing shrugs

1. Stand in front of a mirror, take your arms above your head and lift them towards the ceiling. Use the mirror and try and focus on the movement coming from the back of the shoulders rather than any other part of the arms.

2. Pull the scapula upwards bringing your shoulders to your ears.

Foam Roller Shrugs

1. Come down into Prayer Position (see Sainaa 4, p40), place your arms shoulder width apart resting on top of a foam roller.

2. Slowly roll the foam roller forwards.

3. When you are at your maximum reach, shrug your shoulders to your ears.

9. Serratus Engagement & Activation

Equipment needed: foam roller, resistance band

Four-point Kneeling Serratus Activation

1. Start in four-point kneeling position, making sure your hands are shoulder width apart with fingers facing forwards.

2. Limiting movement in the chest, push the floor away from you. It should feel like you're creating more tension and stabilisation in the shoulder. We want to keep the shoulder blade flush to the thorax (rib cage.)

Serratus Exercise with Resistance Band

This exercise is great for understanding how to feel, how to engage your serratus so you can replicate the same feeling upside down.

1. Just like the foam roller shrugs before, come down into prayer position whilst keeping your arms shoulder width apart resting on the foam roller in front of you.

2. This time you will take a small resistance band between your hands with your palms facing towards each other.

3. When rolling the arms on the foam roller forward, extend your thoracic region (chest) towards the floor as much as possible, then bring it back up.

4. Keep pressing lightly into the foam roller the whole time and keep the shoulders engaged throughout.

10. External Rotation of the Shoulder

Equipment needed: foam roller, resistance band

Four-point Kneeling Regress

1. Start in four-point kneeling position, placing your hands with fingers facing forwards.

2. Pour some weight through your shoulders through your wrists into the floor.

3. Now push the eyes of the elbows (inside of the elbow) forwards. It should feel like you're creating some tension and torque throughout the shoulder girdle.

Resistance Band and Foam Roller Exercise + External Rotation Rep Addition

1. Again, come down into prayer position. Keep the arms shoulder width apart resting on the foam roller.

2. Add the resistance band around the hands but this time with fists facing down towards the floor.

3. Roll the foam roller down and reach out in front of you, extending your chest to the floor as much as possible.

4. When you reach your maximum, turn your fists in towards each other to create an external rotation.

11. Glute Engagement/Corset Rib Technique

Equipment needed: Foam roller, resistance band, mirror (optional)

Glute Engagement

1. Standing by a mirror, contract your glutes for 30 seconds in an isometric hold (not moving).

2. Repeat

Intrinsic core/posterior tilt and ribs in

Position cues before you start the exercise: When you are lying down check that your neck is long, your chin is tucked, your chest is broad. Begin the exercise by pulling the ribs down.

1. Lie on the floor. First engage your rectus abdominus muscle (bottom of the ribs, top of the abdominals). Try and keep the ribs pulled down as much as you can.

2. Now add in your posterior tilt by tucking the pelvis underneath (just as if you were doing a dish or a 'hollow body shape' on the floor).

3. Now take the arms overhead slowly, keep going until you feel you are robbing movement from any other plane (i.e moving the chest) to get your arms to the floor.

4. Stop and bring the arms back up.

Up level: This is to be taken if you're comfortable that you're not compensating from any other part of the body (ribs, lower back) to get the arms resting overhead on the floor. If this is the case then add in lifting the legs off the floor.

When you bring your arms overhead towards the floor take the feet out and straighten the legs out in front of you as in a full dish. Make sure the ribs are still pulled down and you're maintaining that posterior tilt the whole way through.

12. Spotting

Yes you can fall over when you're in a handstand (I get it, the fear is real) but once you learn how to step out to the side safely that danger is minimised. A good spotter will help keep you safe but they will also guide you to improve your acrobatic alignment — they will be your eyes when you are upside down.

Being a good spotter is not easy

Spotting is a skill and if you expect to be spotted well yourself then you have to be a good spotter in return. It is quite technical. In hand-to-hand and other acrobatics a huge part of the class is spotting. Sadly, there are few people who should come to a workshop entitled 'how to spot a handstand #safetyfirst' rather than 'how to do one'.

Being a good spotter is important

When going into a handstand class or starting to train handstands with someone, you are expected to spot well — it is a privilege, it is good practice, it is vital for safety and more than this, spotting well is just good manners. The higher you go in your level, the better a spot you are expected to be.

Being a good spotter for handstands will make you better at handstands

Spotting will help you understand your own handstand shape better, if you take time to be a good spotter you are increasing your own knowledge — for example, if I'm spotting you and you're always closing your shoulders not only can I see it but I can feel it because I may be holding too much of your body weight or constantly trying to push you back into balance. The next time I go up in handstand I can use this information and apply it to my own shape.

Any failure or success you can see in someone else's body will deepen your own understanding of the discipline. If you start taking note of another's practice, this act of observing will make you a better practitioner.

Being a good spotter makes you a nicer person

When learning a skill such as handstand it is fairly integral to work well with others. Training as a pair is useful, you will learn together, finding weaknesses, overcoming challenges and refining your strengths.

The Lesser Spotted Handstand

13. The Lesser Spotted Handstand
aka 'catch and release'

What it works: Learning to stack hips over the shoulders

How it works:

1. The handstander places the arms up by the ears, taking a small lunge they plant the palms on the floor whilst kicking one leg up over the hips, bringing the other leg up to join the first leg.

2. The spotter stands to the side of the handstander. They stand close to the handstander so that the handstander feels secure and they are ready to catch them at the hips.

3. As the handstander starts to kick into handstand, the spotter follows them at the hips and catches them at the top of the handstand, lightly moving them back into balance point if they lose it.

4. The handstander aims to put the same leg that came up last, back on the floor again first, encouraging a controlled descent.

Notes

The spotter should make sure they are catching earlier than they think they want to. That way they can follow the hips on the handstander and catch them earlier rather than later if they kick the hips too far over the shoulders (which happens more than you might think).

14. The Greater Spotted Handstand
aka 'the scissor lift'

This is a trio or partner exercise. The third person is an extra spotter.

What it works:
Learning body awareness in where the 'top' is in handstand. How to stack the hips on top of the shoulders without arching the lower back or sending the leg over the body to get into position. Also decisiveness for a controlled exit.

How it works:

1. The first person gets into downward dog position, raising one leg in the air.

2. The second person positions their body underneath the first person's leg so the leg is resting on their shoulder. The handstander then slowly presses their leg into the spotters shoulder and at the same time brings the other leg up over the hips.

3. The spotter can help by walking in to join the legs together, hips over the shoulders. They will then move to the side so that they are not standing in front of the handstander. The person in the air will then choose a leg and place it towards the floor. This teaches decisiveness and will enable that controlled exit. If you have a third person they will act as an extra spotter behind the handstander.

PART II

THE EXERCISES

The world is full of magic things, patiently waiting for our senses to grow sharper.

- W.B, Yeats

The Exercise Index

1. Internal/External Rotation

solo

What it works: Specific strength, serratus engagement, scapula elevation, preventing shoulder injury, correct alignment, stacking weight, endurance, progressions.

A common mistake is internal rotation. For handstands, everything we do focuses on external rotation for upper body efficiency and safety. You can also repeat this exercise with hands on the ground to get a sense of what it would feel like with weight on the hands.

How it works:

1. Come into a kneeling position, take your arms over your head.
2. For Internal: roll the shoulder blades down the back and create space between the shoulders and ears. There is a downwards motion with no tension in the shoulders — the thumbs move towards each other.
3. For External: hands face the same way, as you externally rotate your shoulders, push the elbows towards each other (imagine 'kissing the elbows'). Elevate the scapula until there is little or no gap between the shoulders and the ears. Imagine 'wrapping' and engaging the serratus muscle as if it were supporting your whole shoulder girdle (which it is!). You should feel that the tension is much more prominent in the shoulder when you externally rotate. The imaginary band between your left and right pec is tight, you want to keep it that way — in internal rotation it is loose.

2. *Alignment Abs*
solo

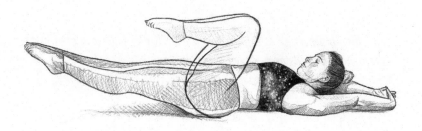

What it works: Alignment, specific strength.

To access correct alignment, a great tester is by seeing if you can keep your arms straight on the floor whilst your head is off the floor, chin to chest, watching your toes. If your arms come off the floor when moving the head, most likely you won't be able to access a perfectly straight line in handstand, yet.

Keeping the lower back flat on the floor is the position you will need to access in handstand.

Basically it works everything in one delicious bundle.

How it works:

1. Lying on the floor, interlink your fingers over your head — palms facing your head with straight arms.
2. Inhale and lift your neck off the mat and look towards your toes.
3. Squish the blueberries — see below!

4. Squeeze the heels together and lift the feet off the floor, tuck the knees in towards the chest on the count of 5.
5. Straighten out the legs on the count of 5.
6. Hold the straight position for 10.
7. Repetitions: 3 holds of 10 equals 1 set

Notes

'Squishing blueberries' is a phrase coined by Kathy Gade, an amazing Acroyoga and handstand teacher from Oakland California. What 'squishing blueberries' means is that you need tuck to the tailbone under to give you a flat back, imagining that you are squishing blueberries on the floor with your back. If this isn't happening, if you feel your lower back is arching — don't lower your legs so much to the floor. If you are still struggling, bend the knees. If you're still struggling, get out of the pose.

3. Pike Up/Straddle Down
solo

What it works: Specific strength — prep for press to handstand (levers and lifts).

How it works:

1. Lying on the floor, take your arms out to the side.
2. Pike your legs up all the way over the top of the head so you are in a shoulder stand position.
3. Straddle the legs actively pushing the feet towards the floor.
4. In a straddle motion draw half circles on the floor so you are back to your starting position.
5. 5 sets and then reverse the motion so you are straddling up and piking down.

Notes

You are welcome to use your hands on the floor to help you with this exercise. Control the descent as you pike down and try to make the sets fluid — try not to let your feet touch the floor in between sets! I like to imagine I am cleaning the floor with my feet so that my straddle always remains active.

4. The Sainaa 4

solo

Sainaa Janchivdorj is the leading teacher of handstands, tumbling and partner acro in London, gracing the circus spaces as well as all of the major studios. He was originally a gymnast, performing as part of a men's troupe and then when he retired at 18 he did what many gymnasts do and kicked ass in the circus world. These 4 exercises designed by Sainaa have become fundamental to my training and to my lesson structure — you just won't find better conditioning for handstands. These exercises are also included as a tribute to the teacher of teachers — seek him out to train in person at The London School of Hand Balancing and Acrobatics.

What it works: Specific strength and alignment.

First position: Handstand shape.

1. Lie on your front with your arms outstretched in handstand position: fingers up, hands shoulder width apart and look at your hands.

2. Body checklist: squeeze your legs together, keep your toes on the ground, squeeze your bum, tuck the pelvis, tighten the abs, pull the chest down and in whilst

trying to push your armpits to the ground.

3. Hold for 20 seconds.

Second position: Prayer Position

1. Sit on your knees, stretch your arms forward with hands together and open your palms like a book. Thighs should be 90° to the ground. Look at your hands. Do not drop your chest. Tighten the abs, pull the chest in and try to make yourself as long as possible from your hands to your bum. Elbows come off the floor.

2. Hold for 20 seconds.

Third position: 10 pike ups: first 5 — feet on floor; second 5 — mini air time.

1. Sit on your heels with knees together. Place hands either side of your knees

2. For the first five, push the floor away from you, straighten your legs leaving the toes on the ground and stack the hips on top of the shoulders. Keep the ears attached to the shoulders. Commit to pushing and stacking, when the position is correct, the weight on your toes will decrease.

3. For the second five, repeat the same but this time straighten the legs with enough energy to lift the toes off the ground by a few inches. The aim is not to kick your legs away but be able to control the height off the ground and control the landing, making it soft on the toes (and ninja silent) by committing to pushing and stacking. Try to avoid bending the knees. Focus on the hips stacking on top of the shoulders and the legs just following behind you.

Fourth position: Long arm handstand plank on toes.

1. Make sure your hands are in a good handstand position (index finger facing forwards, shoulder width apart) keep the toes pointed on the floor.

2. Like a regular plank, don't drop or lift the bum too much. Instead focus on pushing the floor away from you to create a rounded back and hollow chest position.

3. Hold for 20 seconds

Notes

In regular plank position you will notice the scapula protrude slightly and are visible. In handstand plank the scapulae want to be flush, creating a rounded back position. Try not to move the hips at the same time though!

All four positions held for 20 seconds equals one set. To up level, increase time in each exercises or keep to the same time and increase the sets.

5. *The Banana Trio*
spotted

This is a 3 or 4 person exercise (the 4th person is an extra spotter if anyone has the fear of falling over the top.)

What it works: Learning not to arch (banana back).

How it works

1. One person lies face down on the floor in handstand position. They go through a 'body checklist':

- Heels together
- Glutes engaged (tensing the bum)
- Posterior pelvic tilt (tail bone tucked under)
- Abs tight
- A rounded back and hollow chest
- Shoulders superglued to the ears
- Hands and arms shoulder width apart.

2. 2 people stand either side of the person on the floor, each take hands underneath ready to lift them. One hand goes above the hips and one hand goes below the hips on the thighs.

3. Getting their (safe) squat on, they slowly lift the person to handstand. The body gets lifted like a pivot, stacking hips on top of the shoulders.

4. Spotters hold the handstander in their correct shape — with hips on top of the shoulders and shoulders on top of the wrists. They don't have too closed or too open shoulder position. They are not arched in the lower back.

5. Reverse the process slowly back down until the handstander rests on the floor, they should have kept their shape the whole time. If done correctly the handstander will land on the floor with the body as one piece.

Notes

- *Try not to banana (arch) the back (spotters check their form!*
- *Make sure you superglue ears to shoulders to keep correct alignment.*
- *If you touch the floor with the body as one piece then you have done it correctly. If one part of the body touches the floor first (ie the chest) it'll feel as if you're doing 'the worm'. It means you've let something relax in the body (for example your shoulders or your back)*

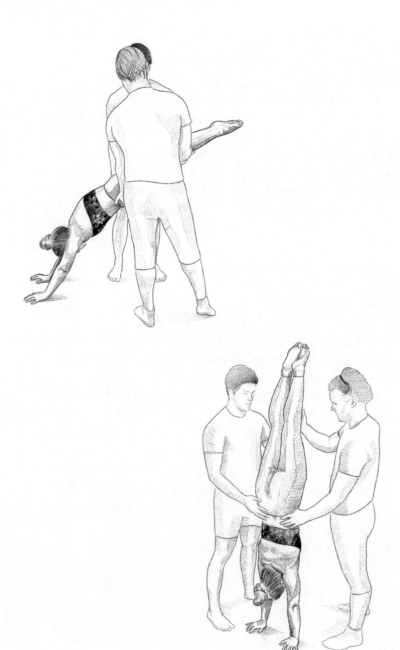

6. Endurance Against The Wall
solo or with spot

Handstands as a goal demand a long journey to get there. Sometimes it's really hard to know whether we are getting any better. This pose works both on measurable progress and correct position which is why I love it so much. Whether we've come to the training session over- or underconfident, this exercise shows us a realistic reflection of our own ability and limitations. Don't be disheartened, just remember to note your time and keep practising it — your time will increase before you know it.

What it works: Endurance in correct alignment.

How it works:

1. Walk your body up the wall so your belly is facing the wall. Walk your hands as close to the wall as is comfortable.
2. Apply the body checklist: Squeeze the heels together, squeeze the bum, tuck the tailbone under to give you a flat back, arms should be shoulder width apart, hands should be facing forwards with external rotation.
3. Lastly, try and make a slight dish shape so your belly is not resting on the wall, only your toes should be resting on the wall —somebody should be able to put a hand in between the wall and your body.
4. Go for your maximum time.

Notes

This is an endurance exercise, keep pushing through the shoulders.
Note your start time and try to increase.

Common mistakes can be resting the belly against the wall so the feet
are coming over the top in a banana back and moving the ears away
from the shoulders in a closed position. Try not to poke the head out,
keep the ears superglued to the shoulders and try not to let the
shoulders drift over the wrists.

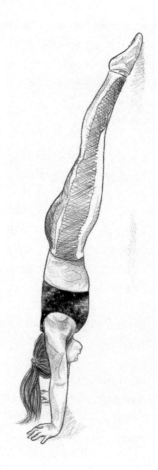

7. *Three Positions On The Wall*

solo or with spot

What it works: Endurance, alignment.

Do each in succession, don't come down in between (even though it's tempting). The positions aren't that technical but what uses the energy is walking between each position. This is a more advanced version of the endurance exercise.

It's also great for body awareness in the air; you have to judge the distance between the wall and your body to hit the correct position. Gabby sees many students that struggle with the transitions and with time and practice start to know exactly where they need their hands to be to get into the correct shape and position.

How it works:

1. Come into your straight endurance position (see exercise above p48)

2. Move into plank position by walking your hands away from the wall so you are at a diagonal angle. Keep the ears attached to the shoulders. Don't pike — you want to lengthen the thighs and keep the lower back connection tight.

3. Your 3rd position is Pike Position (see exercise below p52)

4. Aim for 20 seconds in each position. If you're 'comfortable' do a second set with 20 seconds rest time. If you are feeling ultra sassy, go for a minute in each.

8. Pike Repetitions On The Wall

solo

What it works: Alignment.

How it works:

1. Measure the distance from the wall by sitting in a pike shape against the wall with your legs straight out in front of you. Wherever your heels are, that is where you want to place your hands.

2. Pop your feet up against the wall and bend your knees
    — this will be your 'rest' position.

3. Without moving your feet, up or down the wall,
    straighten your knees for 10 seconds.

4. Rest for maximum 5 seconds.

5. Try 3 sets of 10 seconds.

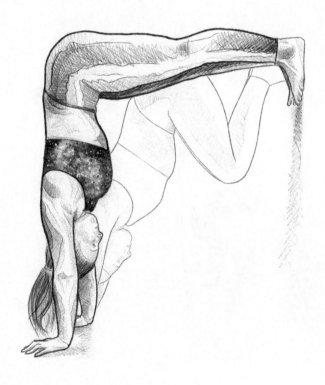

A 'too closed' body position.

This is when the ears move away from the shoulders causing you to make a 'planche' position, the shoulders come too far over the wrists and the head pokes forwards. You'll notice in the image that Gabby's hips are not stacked on top of her shoulders and her shoulders are not on top of her wrists, it's easy to notice that she is not creating a straight line with her body. Gabby should be at a 90° angle with her body to the wall. The above pictures show exactly what we are trying to eliminate in this exercise.

A 'too open' body position.

This is what Gabby calls in class 'hanging off the meat' position. It puts a lot of pressure into the shoulder joint as we're not asking for the big muscles like the serratus to come and help us. In the images above you can see that she is opening the shoulders too much by pushing her chest towards the wall, she's flaring her ribs and it's creating a curved position rather than a straight line from her hips to her shoulders down to her wrists.

The 'Goldilocks' position.

This is when the upper body has a straight line from the hips to the wrists.

Gabby is stacking her shoulders and pushing upwards in a vertical motion. Her ears are superglued to her shoulders and her back is slightly rounded by tucking her tail bone and pulling her ribs in.

Gabby likes to refer to keeping a hollow chest as 'corset rib technique'. Imagine that someone has put a corset around your ribs and they've pulled it really tight, so much that it squeezes all of the air out between your ribs. You'll notice that when you do this motion it should feel like you're closing the distance between the belly button and the sternum.

Think about pushing upwards rather than against the wall. Ideally someone would be able to remove the wall and you would still be stuck in the same shape.

The feeling in your 'Goldilocks' position is that you are having to push and stack a lot to stop your feet sliding off the wall. How do you know that you are doing it right? It is fucking hard.

8a. Variation: Pike With Leg Lift
as before but with leg lifting.

Gabby uses this as an alignment exercise to encourage students to stack their weight correctly. Try not to arch the back and let the leg come too far over the body, instead think about the toes pointing to the ceiling and your upper body position being dead straight and engaged. This will mimic what you want to do away from the wall.

9. Plank To Pike
spotted

*For me this exercise is a lovely little Pre prep exercise for press to
handstand. It introduces what I call 'rolling' technique which you
need to learn to access to have a perfect press to handstand. The hips
will need to be actively rolled up over the shoulders before the feet come
off the floor, this exercise below is great for just isolating the hip-
rolling part without all the other difficult stuff to think about.*

*I also like it for students that may be a little nervous of the 'floor,
face' moment. If the student doesn't follow the correct alignment steps,
it may feel a bit scary so it really forces them to do the right thing in
the body. Especially as someone is holding their feet!*

*It works well for a levelled-up progression from the pike against the
wall exercise as we're having to mimic exactly the same technique and
position but instead adding some strength repetitions in there too.
For intermediate or improver students I would use this as a basic
warm up drill, repeating all 3 lifts in 1 set and then repeating 3
times.*

What it works: Alignment.

How it works:

1. One person makes a regular plank position on the
   floor, pressing into the space in between the shoulder
   blades.

2. The other person lifts them at the heels, feet together.
   The handstander will start rolling their hips up on top
   of the shoulders to get into a nice 'L' position just like

the exercise before. The spotter will follow with the legs in hand until the hips are stacked correctly over the shoulders.

3. If the handstander is pushing and stacking correctly, the spotter will feel some weightlessness in the feet, resting the feet on the stomach, see if the handstander can hold the position for a few seconds before slowly lowering them back down to plank position. *Try not to walk too far away from their body as you'll be holding their ankles!*

4. Repeat x 3

Notes

The person in handstand should be trying to resist the bum and hips coming over the shoulders or the shoulders coming over the wrists and the head/ears separating from the shoulders. We're looking for a perfect 'L shape.'

10. Consistency Drills
spotted or solo

What it works: Consistency, alignment

This exercise is not for balance, the focus is on consistently hitting the right position for handstand (hips over shoulders) so the repetitions should be plenty and short (not focusing on balancing the handstand at the top).

How it works:

1. Walk or kick into handstand, make sure you stack the hips over the shoulders each time.

2. Do this 3 times and if you have a spot, ask them to allow you to find balance for the 4th repetition, staying up in the air for 10 seconds. This 4th repetition will help work your balance, endurance and alignment.

Notes

For more advanced students, you can do multiple sets of 4 repetitions changing the gaze point or the hand position for the 4th repetition every time. Example (right) the handstander is spotted while looking at the toes.

For those that can balance a handstand correctly, still practise consistency but use the 4th set as a balance set without a spotter.

11. Nico's Tuck

(aka 'tuck against the wall')
solo or with spot

This was taught to me by Nico (see p6). This one can be a bit of a kerfuffle, but do keep with it. You just have to work out how far you want your hands away from the wall as everyone is going to be different (body type, flexibility etc.)

What it works: Alignment, shape

This is a great exercise for eliminating movement in the shoulders when kicking/jumping/straddling/pressing (and entrance) into handstand. It's really common that people move the shoulders when practicing various entrances into handstand. If they are constantly closing the shoulders (most common) then they are forever chasing to get the hips on top of the shoulders and having to snake their body into correct alignment and balance. By learning to isolate movement in the shoulders they create efficiency and consistency in stacking the hips on top of shoulders so they can get into correct handstand shape using much less energy.

How it works

1. Move yourself a couple of hands distance away from the wall and walk your body up the wall so your belly is facing it, but not as close to the wall as the endurance position.

2. Squeezing your knees and your heels together, slowly slide your feet down the wall. Bring your knees as close in towards your chest and stomach in a tuck shape.

3. Now without moving your ears away from your shoulders and limiting all movement in your shoulders,

slide your feet up to straight position again. I repeat:
Do *not* move your shoulders.

Set and reps: Beginners — 2 sets of 5. Intermediate —
1 set of 10. Advanced — 3 sets of 12.

Notes

*Wear socks, it's easier. This is a technical exercise, not an endurance
one — if you feel you are losing your technique come down and regain
some energy to start again. For the common mistakes see the figures
on too open/too closed/Goldilocks' position on p54-6.*

*Spot at the hips, guiding the hips and blocking shoulders if the
handstander is not confident in the exercise.*

The Basic Shapes

12. Tuck

What it works: Shape.

How it works:

1. Starting from a crouched position, keeping your shoulders blocked, round your back and glue your ears to your shoulders.

2. Bend your knees and jump your hips over your shoulders in a tucked ball position. Once your hips are over your shoulders you should be on technical balance point.

3. Slowly tuck back down to the floor.

Try 3 sets of jumping into tuck. Don't worry about balancing the handstand, just keep trying to stack the hips on top of the shoulders.

Notes

Level up by starting from kneeling on the floor and then jumping into the tuck.

Ideally we're trying to keep our knees tucked as close to our chest as possible, eliminating the bum from coming over the shoulders. This heavily depends on flexibility, compression and specific strength.

13. Tuck Travelling Sequence

This is a great preparation exercise for jumping into tuck handstand. If you are struggling with tuck — don't panic, it is super difficult! Many many people struggle to stack the hips over the shoulders whilst keeping the legs close to the stomach and chest. A great way to practise this, and to remove some of the pressure, is to do some bunny hops in a line.

What it works: Preparation for a tuck handstand.

How it works:

1. Start with a bunny hop. The hips can stay low and the hands lunge out in front. The hips then come with you into a baby jump joining the feet next to your hands.

2. For the second repetition, the hands are now placed on the floor, the feet are closer to the hands and we're aiming to jump the hips up on top of the shoulders.

3. Repeat 5 times.

Notes

You can apply this travelling sequence to all of the basic shapes.

14. Straddle

What it works: Shape

How it works:

1. Starting from a crouched position, place your hands on the floor shoulder width apart.

2. Jump your hips on top of the shoulders, making sure the ears are not coming unglued from the shoulders and the shoulders are not coming too far over the wrists. When jumping we're just changing the shape of the legs, think about getting the hips over the shoulders first, the legs are going to follow by coming straight out behind you.

3. Try 3 sets of 3 repetitions of jumping into straddle handstand. Again, not focusing on the balance, just building the muscle memory of stacking the hips over the shoulders whilst being able to make different shapes with the legs.

Notes

We're really focusing on the technique of getting into these shapes rather than the shape itself. You can play with how the shape actually looks afterwards by working on specific flexibility. You can up level by starting from your knees.

15. Pike

What it works: Shape

How it works:

1. Starting from a crouched position, place the hands on the floor shoulder width apart.

2. Jump the hips on top of the shoulders whilst making sure the shoulders and ears stay attached and the head doesn't come away from the shoulders. Don't come too far over the wrists. When focusing on jumping the hips over the shoulders let the legs come together in a straight pike shape behind you.

3 sets of 3 repetitions.

Notes

The legs should stay together in a pike handstand and you want to imagine that you're leaving the legs behind. Focus on stacking the hips over the shoulders, then any shape you make with the legs will not require any extra effort, due to you already being on technical balance point.

People always think you need strong abs or there is some sort of magic in the pike position, I promise it's just technique. Once your hips are on top of your shoulders, you can do whatever decoration you like with the legs.

16. Endurance In Basic Shapes

What it works: Balance, endurance and shape.

This exercise is great for intermediate/improver level students as it really starts to teach them how to 'fight' for the balance. If you're at the level where you still need a spot because of the length of time this exercise is held but can access all the shapes well, get your spotter to do 'light spotting' which is only catching you when you're falling. Solo or lightly assisted, this exercise is great for highlighting whether you're balancing your handstand correctly (in the hands and not moving parts of the body to stay on balance) and also how to fight for it.

How it works:

1. Straight shape - 10 secs
2. Straddle shape - 10 secs
3. Diamond shape - 10 secs
4. Tuck shape - 10 secs

Equals 1 set. Repeat 3 times.

Regress:

Halve the time to 5 secs per shape. Exclude one shape from the set. Gabby suggests removing the tuck position as most people find it the hardest especially as it's the last shape in the set.

Try to keep the connection in the lower back strong the whole time. It is really common to want to arch the back when in straddle position and diamond position; if this happens the rest of the alignment starts failing (shoulders, ribs etc.) then it becomes harder to stack the weight

71

and feel where the balance should be. If you're working alone, videoing yourself is a great way to see what you're doing when you can't feel it. If you have a training buddy, let them tell you when your alignment starts failing, they can give you clues to which body part is sinking.

There should be very little movement in the mid section of the body. The upper body stays within its solid handstand alignment and technique, the hands balance and the legs decoratively move between each shape.

17. *Balance Exercise*
solo

Pre-requisite: if you don't have a straight shape in handstand, this isn't for you yet. Remember there is no balance before alignment, always balance after alignment.

What it works: Balance.

Getting your feet off the wall without using your feet and forcing the balance technique into the fingers rather than using the body to balance your handstand.

How it works

1. Kick up against the wall so your back is facing the wall. For this exercise you are allowed to have a small arch in the lower back but make sure the bum isn't resting against the wall.

2. Using the upper body try and get the feet and legs off the wall.

Point 1) Fingers. Use your fingers as if you're pulling the floor towards you.

Point 2) Shoulders. Assuming you're not a beginner now, it's more than just a pushing up action (or pushing the floor away from you), the action is now pushing up and 'locking in.' Engage the pec muscles, the serratus and the lats. The action is an external rotation of the shoulders — it might be helpful to think of screwing in a lightbulb.

Point 3) Chest/Ribs. Use the corset ribs technique. Imagine someone has wrapped a corset around your ribs and pulled it tight so it feels as if all the air between your ribs has been squished out. You'll be making a hollow chest and rounded back position. It should feel as if you're shortening the space between your sternum and belly button (of course staying as tall as possible and having your shoulders open the whole time).

3. Using the upper body, activate and pour energy into those 3 points to get your feet off the wall. When you've managed this, try and put all of the focus into the fingers to keep you in handstand. If you manage to get your feet off the wall and then you end up coming down it means you haven't kept extension throughout your body.

Try not to think about 'balancing a handstand' and concentrate on following the steps.

In visualising getting their body away from the wall, people often think of leaning away from the wall. This means you end up using other parts of the body to get the feet off, like the feet or lower back. Instead, try and visualise staying close to the wall and scaling up it!

18. The Handstand 'Feeling' Exercise
solo

'It is not a dance'

— Alexander Gavrilov aka Russian handstand god

What it works: This is a great exercise to mimic the feeling in handstand but with your feet still on the ground.

How it works:

1.   Come to a standing position, lean your weight forward without breaking the line in your body. What you should notice is that your toes start to cling on to the floor to stop you from taking a step.

2.   Now bring the weight back a tiny bit. You should feel like your toes are clinging on but it's not as extreme as before. There should be a nice amount of contact and pressure on the ball of the foot.

A really common question from my students is 'how do I save my handstand when the weight goes into the heels of my hands?'

The answer is…you can't.

Well, you physically can but it involves a lot of bent arms and your body snaking its way back into correct alignment and balance.

If you are falling onto the heels of your hands often it is because of one of the following two reasons:

a) You haven't learnt correct balance technique *yet* and don't know how to 'save' the handstand.

b) You are not in correct alignment which reflects where the weight is in your handstand.

If ever you feel like you want to walk in your handstand to find your balance, come down and start again. Ideally we don't want to create these movement patterns as our bodies will remember and repeat them. They can often become habits and you may have to spend double the time and practice undoing it before you can move on.

PART III

THE TRAINING PLANS

The drugs don't work.

- The Verve.

1. How To Use The Training Plans

Choosing Your Plan

The training plans go in a gentle curve from hard to harder so if you are just beginning your journey begin at number 1 and slowly progress through them. There is no shame in repeating a favourite plan until you are confident you are strong enough to move onto the next. We've left some empty templates for you to create your own and we've added some explanations of the plan's outline so you can see the method behind the magic/madness.

Training Focus

In yoga we often work with an intention. This can be very broad, for example my intention today might be to 'overcome obstacles' or it could be very specific, for example to 'breathe into my hips'. For a handstand training session we have suggested working with, at least initially, a body-centric intention: we've called this the 'training focus'. As your training progresses you will find your own specific goals for each session. If you write this down at the top of your plan you are more likely to remember and key in very particularly to this specific skill you are trying to hone in the time you have available.

Dynamic Warm Up (5-10 mins)

Everyone has their own way of warming up. I love to run, Gabby does (really really) not like to run. We are aiming to raise the body temperature and increase the blood flow. You might prefer jumping jacks, skipping for a minute or dancing to Taylor Swift. No? Our favourite dynamic warm up is 'the pyramid set' (Gabby is almost unbeatable). This pyramid set is 4 exercises done in consecutive sets of 5 / 4 / 3 / 2 / 1. A great combination is jumping jacks followed by squat jumps, press ups and tuck crunches. Try and do these as fast as you can, preferably competing with a friend. The warm up should last around 5-10 minutes depending on how much time you have. A dynamic warm up is important because it wakes up your receptors, improving your performance, helping to prevent injury and making your practice more efficient.

Joint Mobilisation

It is important to mobilise before you start a training session; it helps to lubricate the joints with synovial fluid, making your practice more comfortable. When you mobilise the joints work from the bottom up, rolling the ankles, knees, hips, rib cage, shoulders and ending with some slow neck rolls.

Specific Conditioning

For this section, choose from
- *Alignment Abs (p37)*
- *Pike Up/Straddle Down (p39)*
- *Sainaa 4 (p40)*
- *Banana Trio (p45)*
- *Pike Repetitions on the Wall (p53)*

Pillars

For this section, depending on how much time you have, you might want to focus on just one or two exercises from one or two pillars. For example, if playing with endurance choose Endurance Exercise (well, duh).

Knowledge is Power

Keeping a record of your plans will help you see your progression. It says 'Endurance Exercise — 3 reps of 30 seconds each' on the plan but you did 45 seconds? Write that down and next time you come to your training you will know to up your expectations. It is also really good fun to look back over the last few months of training and see how far you've come or, if you haven't done any in awhile, to see how awesomely motivated you were just a few weeks previously.

Rest

Handstands take a long time, and a lot of effort, to master. Do the work but also allow your body time to integrate the information — much of which will be new. This book contains technical information on how to improve your handstand technique, shape and alignment. It also contains exercises designed to help you build up specific strength for your handstands. In building up this strength, you will be building muscle and creating profound physiological change.

This is a journey both of mind and of body, one of these components so often charging ahead while the other follows cautiously behind. Give yourself the opportunity to listen to your body — it is wise. This is a skill in itself. If it is telling you to ease off, ease off. Give yourself time, give yourself rest, and most importantly... give yourself a break. We've also included some simple restorative poses. Not every day is a training day, if it's one of 'those' days consider some gentle breathing, meditation or one of the poses in the 'Restorative' section.

Training Plan 1
30 minutes

Training Focus: *Hand position and keeping external rotation when in handstand position*

Dynamic Warm Up (5 mins)

Joint Mobilisation

Specific Conditioning

Internal/External Rotation (p36) - 5 reps each
Alignment Abs (p37) - 1 set

Pillars

Specific Strength: Sainaa 4 - holding each position for a slow 10 seconds (p40)
Endurance: Endurance Exercise - Belly to wall for maximum time without compromising shape (p48)

Stretch/Mobility

Open Bar Stretch: Take hands shoulder width apart on a bar or ledge, push your chest down towards the floor as much as possible and then without moving the shoulders too much tuck the tailbone under, tighten the abs and pull the chest in very slightly. You should feel an isolated shoulder stretch. Repeat 3 times for 10 seconds each.

In a kneeling position, take fingers towards the knees then take one hand and place it over the top of the other hand. Nice and slowly bend your elbow and peel your palm off the floor as much as is comfortable. Hold for 5. Repeat on other side.

Training Plan 2

30 minutes

Training Focus: *Gaze point*

Dynamic Warm Up / Joint Mobilisation

Specific Conditioning

Hip flexor training - sitting in straddle position place both of your hands either side of one knee. Keeping your palms flat on the floor and your back as straight as possible, lift leg for 10 reps (keeping your back as straight as possible) and then on the last one hold for 10. Repeat on other leg.

Pillars

Specific Strength: Sainaa 4 (see Training Plan 1)
Endurance: Belly to wall max time (p48)
Pike Reps: 3 sets of 10 seconds (p52)

Stretch

Strap shoulder mobilisation - hold a strap with your hands wider than shoulder width. Starting with your hands towards the floor at the front and keeping your arms straight the whole time, circle your arms overhead and as far back as you can, then bring them back to the starting position. Repeat for 5 repetitions.

For a further 3 repetitions shorten the gap between your hands — repeat the exercise but this time touching on the edge of your comfort zone. Note: Try not to move your chest or elevate your shoulders too much. Make sure one shoulder isn't leading. If it is uncomfortable, widen the gap between the hands. Make two fists with the fingers closed, put the two fists together and put them facing down, knuckles together. Now try and slowly straighten the elbows.

Training Plan 3

45 minutes

Training Focus: Decisiveness

Dynamic Warm Up

Joint Mobilisation

Specific Conditioning

Shoulder prehabilitation: Take a resistance band, come into Prayer Position (p41) but with hands shoulder width apart holding the band. Keep the chest relaxed to the floor. Try not to move the shoulders too much and lift one arm for 3 repetitions, repeat taking arm out to the side. Repeat on the other side.

Pillars

Alignment: Pike Reps Against the Wall - 3 x 10 secs

Consistency: Kicking up to handstand x 4, last one try to hold in correct alignment for 10 seconds. 3 repetitions.

Stretch

Open bar stretch (see Training Plan 1)

'The Vogue' - sitting on the floor, take tops of the hands on hips with elbows facing outwards as if you are doing a chicken dance (!). Keeping the hands where they are, bend the knees and pop the elbows on the inside of the knees. Squeeze the knees in towards each other to increase the stretch.

Training Plan 4
45 minutes

Training Focus: *Remembering to breathe*

Dynamic Warm Up

Joint Mobilisation

Specific Conditioning

Shoulder prehabilitation (see Training Plan 3)

Active compression exercise: Sit on the floor. Lift your legs straight into the air into a 'V' position and take the hands off the floor (like boat pose in yoga).

Make a mental note of your position and then slowly lower your feet down into a dish shape (or half boat pose). Bring the body back up to find the original 'V' shape. Keep actively pulling your thighs to your stomach and keep your back as straight as possible.

Hip flexor training (see Training Plan 2) with up level of doing both legs at the same time. Lift the legs and move the legs in little circles for 10 and then hold for 10.

Pillars

Alignment: 3 Positions Against the Wall - 20 seconds each (p50)

Consistency: Kicking up in handstand x 4, last one try to hold in correct alignment

Shape: Nico's Tuck: 10 tuck reps against the wall (2 sets of 5 reps) (p62)

Stretch

Massage forearms with knees: come down onto knees, place your bent arm in front of you, palm up. Take the same knee and make rolling circular motions from the top of the forearm all the way down to the wrist.

Nervy stretch: stand with your body side on to a wall. Place the hand palm facing up, fingers towards the floor. Hand and shoulder should be in the same line. Slowly turn your body and head away from the arm. You should feel a 'nervy' sensation down the arm.

Training Plan 5
60 minutes

Training Focus: Control

Alignment focus: *hollow ribs and serratus engagement*

Dynamic Warm Up / Joint Mobilisation

Specific Conditioning

Alignment Abs (p37)
Sainaa 4 - hold for 20 seconds each position

Pillars

Alignment: Endurance Exercise, belly to wall with a shape focus. 3 x 30 secs. (p48)

Balance: Balance Exercise x 3 reps (p73)

Level up combo for endurance, shape and balance for anyone who can already balance a handstand (or has a spotter) do 10 seconds each of straight handstand, straddle, diamond and then back to straight.

Stretch

Open bar stretch (3 x 10 secs) (See Training Plan 1)

Active box spilt stretch with resistance band (Deuserband): sitting in straddle position facing the wall so feet touch the wall, take the strap around the lower back, in front of the knee and around the feet. Put your hands behind you and tuck the pelvis underneath so you're not arching and slowly edge your hips towards the wall, closing the triangular gap. Do this for 1 minute.

Training Plan Template 1
A chance to document your own training

Training Focus:

Alignment Focus:

Dynamic Warm Up:

Joint Mobilisation:

Specific Conditioning:

Pillars:

Stretch:

Training Plan Template 2

Training Focus:

Alignment Focus:

Dynamic Warm Up:

Joint Mobilisation:

Specific Conditioning:

Pillars:

Stretch:

Training Plan Template 3

Training Focus:

Alignment Focus:

Dynamic Warm Up:

Joint Mobilisation:

Specific Conditioning:

Pillars:

Stretch:

Training Plan Template 4

Training Focus:

Alignment Focus:

Dynamic Warm Up:

Joint Mobilisation:

Specific Conditioning:

Pillars:

Stretch:

Training Plan Template 5

Training Focus:

Alignment Focus:

Dynamic Warm Up:

Joint Mobilisation:

Specific Conditioning:

Pillars:

Stretch:

----

2. Rest Day Restorative Practice

1. Sit on your knees, you can sit on a bolster or block to make yourself more comfortable — remember this is all about finding a place of ease and comfort. In yoga-speak this is called hero pose or *virasana.*

2. As you sit start to deepen your breath. If it helps to add a count to the breath, start with inhale for 2 and exhale for 4; you might wish to increase it to 3 and 6 or even 4 and 8.

3. Let the breath wash over your whole body. This is a practice without expectation or goal; if anything, it is a check in. Take your hands to your belly and start to notice how the belly rises and falls with the breath. We often hold tension in our bellies, without judgement start to notice any feelings that bubble up. Whether it is anger, happiness, peace or frustration just notice these feelings and let them pass.

4. As you continue your practice you might want to add a simple and silent mantra to your breath such as inhale 'I am calm' exhale 'I am allowed to be vulnerable' or inhale 'I am strong' exhale 'I am soft'.

5. Choose one or more of the following poses. Stay for 5-20 minutes before easing yourself out of your rest as gently as you entered it. Take a few minutes in a seated position to contemplate your practice and thank your body for all that it does.

1. CHILD'S POSE

balasana

Equipment: mat, block (optional), bolster (optional), blanket (optional).

How it works:

1. Option 1: Take your knees as wide as your yoga mat. Take your arms either in front of you (as illustrated) or behind, letting the backs of the hands rest on the mat.

2. If your neck feels strained add a block under the forehead.

3. To add support, roll up a blanket and place it either in between the hips and ankles or under the ankles.

4. Option 2: If you have a yoga bolster place it in between the thighs, close to the pelvis. Many students prefer to elevate the bolster with a yoga block or to add another bolster on top.

2. WATERFALL POSE

vipariti karani

Equipment: mat, bolster (optional), yoga strap (optional)

How it works:

1. Lie down by a wall with your hips as close as you can get them to the wall itself. Make sure you have sufficient padding underneath your head with a blanket or small pillow.

2. Bend your knees and press your feet against the wall to elevate your hips; there is an option here to slide a blanket or bolster under the hips.

3. Option to put a yoga strap around your thighs to reduce the energy needed to keep them together.

4. Take your hands either side of you or on your belly. Melt.

95

3. CORPSE POSE

savasana

Equipment: mat, bolster (optional), blanket (optional).

How it works:

1. Option 1: Lie yourself down gently with your back on a mat. Make sure you feel supported.

2. If your neck feels strained at all add a slim block or a rolled blanket under it.

3. Option 2: To create ease in the lower back put a bolster underneath your knees.

4. Put some relaxing music on — whale songs get a bad rep but they really do work.

PART
IV

THE STORY

You are stronger than you think you are

— Larry Scholz, Founder of Rocket Yoga

Heyam dukham anagatam.

Pain that is yet to come can be avoided.

— Yoga Sutra II:16, Patanjali

1. The Injury

There were days when this book was fuelled by the freshest and greenest of organic avocados, delicately mashed, framed by poached eggs, scattered with pomegranate seeds and lovingly stacked on locally-sourced granary toast. There were also days (more than I'd care to admit) when this book was fuelled by builders' tea and Galaxy bars. Those were the days that didn't get put on Instagram. Today was one of those days.

"Er, what did you call me?"

"You know, a muggle — a non-circus person."

Gabby had spent the morning flicking through social media, wincing at the attempted high-flying acrobatics of these enthusiastic 'muggles' as she called us, I think with equal amusement and exasperation. The night before she'd sent me a video of two athletic amateurs throwing each other around trying to handstand on each others' hands. To an untrained (i.e. my) eye the couple looked impressive, graceful even. A giddy high-five and a gleeful "Whooop!" upon landing did, I suppose, indicate that perhaps their technique wasn't quite as consistent as the 30 second snippet might suggest. Gabby's comment to me below the video read: "[wide-eyed emoji] 2 more years [wincing emoji]."

Apparently it was us 'muggles' that were more prone to injury when attempting our Instagram-worthy feats, whether that was due to ignorance of technique or puppy-like overconfidence it usually ended in a crack, or a ping or a 'that was really lucky'.

The expert and undefeated Japanese swordsman Miyamoto Musashi wrote in his book *The Book of Five Rings* that 'all injury comes from immature strategy' but the thing is it wasn't just us amateurs that were hurting; training at the local circus space I'd heard tales of aerialists that had been out for months with rotator cuff issues, tumblers with torn cruciate ligaments due to dynamic twisting, pole dancer performers suffering torn hamstrings and dislocated shoulders. It seemed that no matter how skilled you were, some injury comes from just dumb bad luck.

We'd taken over Gabby's mum's dining room table with snacks, snaking wires and stacks of highlighted articles on yoga anatomy (and chocolate). I had a specific question I wanted answered — if I was going to tackle this handstand mountain I wanted to know about injury. How was I, muggle that I am, going to remain injury-free on this upside down adventure? I liked my wrists — with them I could do handy tricks like open doors or buy things with one-click off Amazon. Not quite as impressive as being able to balance on one finger but I'd wager a tad more useful.

Gabby was gentle with my concerns. "In my experience there are two ends of the spectrum: There are the professionals — training hard and putting particular strain on certain parts of their body. That part of the body will sometimes sadly crack under the pressure and they will injure themselves. They are at one end of the spectrum.

There are those who exist in the middle of the spectrum, those who are not professionals but who train intelligently, prepare and condition the body well for their movements and understand the techniques they are using. Brilliant — be one of these people.

Then there are those at the other end of this spectrum. Those who attempt higher level movements without preparing the body, without strengthening and without stretching. These folks are also very likely to get injured. Please don't be one of these people."

I nodded, silently promising either to do zero handstanding or first become a super conditioned acrobot. She softened. "Look, no one can predict injuries and you often couldn't have done anything to avoid them happening. They will come at the most unlikely, and often at the most annoying, of times. We can only try to learn from them, if and when they happen."

"But what about you?" I asked, surreptitiously stealing the last square of Galaxy. "Have you ever got injured doing circus?"

I once accidentally asked a gold-medal winning Olympic trampolinist whether she considered herself 'sporty' (to clarify, I did not know she was a gold-medal winning Olympic trampolinist at the time). Gabby stopped typing and looked at me with that exact same expression.

"When I was 19 I jumped out of a window."

I wish I had met Gabby BC (before circus). Fractious and distracted, Gabby was something of a rebel. Having been excluded from school she was on a search for something (or someone) to challenge her. She also had electric pink hair (think the pop star Pink circa 1999) and half a dozen more piercings than she does currently.

Circus did for Gabby what it does for so many, it humbled her. This circus adventure took her and her co-conspirators James and Bryn, to the South of France. The three had met in Circomedia, a performance arts school in Bristol. They were fresh out of school at 18, obsessed with getting better and wanting to cut their teeth on the infamously strict French circus scene. James, sporty and obsessive, and Bryn, fresh-eyed and silently driven. After circus, James became a ski instructor and is now climbing in New Zealand; Bryn would go on to join a sought-after teeterboard troupe first in France then in Montréal, before leaving circus due to a serious head injury. But for now they found themselves with Gabby, three very small fish in a very large French pond.

All three musketeers were accepted into Balthazar circus school in Montpelier, Southern France, the first British students ever to be invited onto their programme. After one year there, all three applied to the Ecole Nationale Du Cirque De Rosny-Sous-Bois (ENACR). Gabby and James didn't get in, Bryn did.

Gabby now needed to find another school to continue her acro education. One of the schools she applied to was a picturesque tented circus school set in the lush green hills above Cannes called Piste D'Azur. Gabby had applied as a flyer but she was now flying solo, a flyer without her base — she was, temporarily, grounded. Piste D'Azur agreed to accept her but there was a catch — she would only be allowed in on the proviso that she switched disciplines. Instead of hand-to-hand she would now be training in Hungarian teeterboard. Some people reading this will already know what a teeterboard is, I did not and the first time I saw it on YouTube my breath caught in my chest — for teeterboard an acrobat performs gymnastic dismounts (somersaults, backflips and all other kinds of fancy tumbles) from what is essentially a seesaw. It looked terrifying. Gabby agreed, "I wasn't a gymnast, I couldn't tumble and I was (and still am) terrified of the teeterboard."

It was now the end of her first year in France and her first year at circus school. She was exhausted and, even more debilitatingly, broke. Thankfully she had a whole summer before the second year started so she headed to Bryn's family farm in Normandy to practise, gain some funds and recoup some well-needed sleep. Gabby also began work on a mission; if she was going to be able to teeter she needed to work on something had been chasing her all year: her fear. She needed to learn how to jump.

Gabby tells the story of her jump in the slightly disembodied voice that people use when they discuss a gap year ayahuasca trip; as if it was them and not them all at the same time. "It was so unlike me, I think about it now, even with more training, and I'm like 'I would *never* do that!'" Even as acrobat Bryn looked on with a shake of his wary head, Gabby fixed her sights on jumping out of a second storey converted barn window.

If she could jump out of that window, then she would have won. The Fear would be conquered, she would go back to circus school, become a teeterboard artist and that would be that…

Rural France not having a plethora of accessible emergency services, Gabby was bundled hastily into the back of Bryn's parents' car — a pillow wrapped tightly around her foot to catch the steady flow of blood dripping from her heel. At the hospital, even though she was doped up to the eyeballs on morphine, Gabby remembers the nurses rushing out of her room to catch Bryn's dad who had almost fainted upon seeing them stitch up her foot.

"Nobody really knew what was going on or how serious my injury was," Gabby shrugs. Only upon returning to the UK did she discover that only a few surgeons in the world would have actually known the specifics of how to treat her injury. As fate would have it, one of them was her resident surgeon at Bristol hospital.

Gabby leans in, insistent. "I will forever be in debt to him. He was honest, informed and blunt — exactly what I needed right then." She peers earnestly into my notebook, which I shield by habit, as if to make sure that the surgeon professor was getting a suitable write-up.

The surgeon looked up from Gabby's x-rays, candour and concern etched across his features. The procedure had a higher success rate if done within 10 days, it had been months before Gabby had hobbled back to Bristol only to be told that there was a lengthy waiting list for her surgery.

"I'd come in on crutches and I remember the startled look on the doctors' faces when they saw I was even partially weight-bearing. The scans of my ankle looked like one of those impossible jigsaw puzzles you give people you don't like as prank gifts. Here, have a shattered calcaneum. Merry Christmas!"

"I had a private consultation with the surgeon who by some miracle had himself developed the surgery 25 years ago. He told us there was a chance, but that the risk of infection was increased due to the wound having to be reopened and the introduction of metal supports."

Three choices, all not looking particularly appealing, were laid out: risk losing her leg by having the more advanced surgery; fusing the joint so that her mobility would be limited to (the hospital staff's words) 'getting out of the way of an oncoming bus' and the final option being to not have surgery at all and therefore having no idea whether she would walk again.

Given the choices available Sara, Gabby's mum, understandably wanted to go for the final option. Take the unknown and avoid the risk of her daughter having to have her leg amputated. Gabby went to the gym that evening and then woke up knowing that she should have the riskier surgery. That morning the phone rang, and it was the surgeon.

"The surgeon phoned my mum, he had daughters my age and said that he would advise them to get the surgery. He also said that he would go away for 2 weeks to study the case." The surgery was booked, and Gabby's parents sold their home to pay for it.

Learning to walk again was a long, wobbly road. To reduce risk of infection, Gabby had gone on a serious health kick — binning the cigarette packets and curbing her infamous Jaffa cake addiction. She was in hospital three years running on Christmas Day, always visited by her surgeon. "I always send him a Christmas card, just letting him know what I'm getting up to — learning to walk on my feet again so I could make a career standing on my hands!"

Surgery however was only the beginning of the journey. Gabby had damaged receptors and the foot was stuck at an awkward angle. Due in part to her many doses of general anaesthetic and a loss of muscle mass she had also shrunk to a feeble six stone (and Gabby is tiny, but not so tiny that six stone is healthy). She began working earnestly for hours a day on her physiotherapy, flexing and extending her foot trying to grapple back the mobility and strength that she had lost.

Her zeal was rewarded. Gabby wiggles her feet proudly under the cafe table. "Look" (wiggle wiggle) "the flexion on my damaged foot is now better than that of my left."

Six months into recovery Gabby got a call from Bryn. He was going into his second year now at ENACR, the school Gabby had failed to get into the year before. He said they needed a flyer, and Gabby fitted the description, a perfect if slightly broken piece in their circus puzzle.

"I arrived at the school on crutches for a two week trial period and lied through my teeth about how I'd got my injury. They told me that if they couldn't find anyone else, I was in." Much to her physiotherapist's dismay, the deans at ENACR couldn't find anyone better and Gabby left for her second year of professional circus training a little while later, ready to fly after almost a year of not being able to walk.

The Banker
Name: Susan
Age: 30s

Poor Fear, she does have a tendency to get in the way. Imagine all the fun that could be had from that poorly-constructed rollercoaster or going over to talk to that cute girl by the bar. In Pixar's film Inside Out, *the golden sparkly Joy can't seem to understand what role mopey blue Sadness has in human experience. Fear is perhaps equally misunderstood. She is an occasional hindrance for sure but she is also our armoured angel — our first defence when things are about to go very very badly wrong.*

We've all experienced it. Having detected an object of fear our body tenses up — our primal defence mechanisms automatically switched on and dialled up. We typically shoot our shoulders up to our ears and grip our jaw tight. Blood starts pumping to our getaway-fast muscles and away from our rational thought process; our heart rate elevates, our pupils dilate, our peripheral vision shuts down — we are ready to face anything. Well, anything that has pointy teeth and sharp claws anyway; when it comes to our modern aggressors (a deadline, a traffic jam, a surprise inversion option in a yoga class) fear can become more of a hindrance than a help.

A way to temper and dial down these symptoms is of course to simply take a deep breath. We may still be fearful, but encouraging deep full breaths should at least alleviate the hyperventilation. Yogis love a good, long, noisy breath. This breathing in and out through the nose, paired with a slight restriction of the throat is, Ash tells me, called ujjayi, *the victorious breath. It sounds like the sea and is almost as powerful. This tidal noise works as a pace-setter for the practice, a way to sync with the group in a class setting as well as a handy tool to fall back on if you find yourself holding your breath in a sticky moment. A sticky moment like when your teacher asks you to go upside down.*

Susan has been a private student of mine for a while. She works at one of the big banks in a high pressure job that requires her to sit behind a desk most of the day making very big important decisions.

We met when she started to attend my group sessions, she would come once a week and cry every time. Most of us have had a teary moment in savasana *or in frog pose and this is completely normal, as much in acrobatics as it is in yoga. Stretching accesses emotional triggers, and we all have our emotional hotspots. For Susan it was her shoulders and her back.*

Susan had a lot of fear and a lot of frustration. The class environment was amplifying the pressure that Susan was putting on herself: 'if everyone is able to do it, why can't I?' We've all felt overwhelmed in a class; the feeling of not wanting to draw attention to ourselves, to the fact that we are scared and unsure of how to handle the emotions that are being brought up.

Susan was scared yes, but she was also determined to go upside down. Susan had set a high bar for herself to reach. Her fast-paced banker's brain was overthinking everything and as such she was having a crisis of confidence. Sometimes the more skilled a person, the more pressure they apply on themselves.

The way that Susan and I deal with her fear in our sessions is to pause and then question. Being afraid of handstands is completely normal — there could be fear of going over the top; a fear of elbows buckling under your own weight; the fear of stepping away from the wall; the fear of not being able to do it; and my favourite and most common of all, the fear of looking like a tit in front of everyone. But in order to understand this fear, we need to pinpoint it. For Susan we use a step by step technique; at what point do the handstands become fearful? When we are lunging into them? When we are in the air? What is it we are actually afraid of?

If you are fearful there is no need to jump into the deep end of the inversion pool. Take time to explore the shape and investigate how it feels in your body. You can find it by working on specific handstanding strength (p37) or finding yourself lifted and helped into a handstand using a scissor lift (p32); harnessing your innate power and discovering strength that you never even knew you had!

Susan's Handstand Pillars:

Specific Strength: 1/5
Endurance: 2/5
Alignment: 2/5
Consistency: 1/5
Balance: 0/5
Mobility/Flexibility: 3/5
Shape: 0/5

Susan's Handstand Exercises:

Prehab: Prayer position in Sainaa 4 (sphinx version - arms straight out shoulder width apart) x3 one arm upward repetitions followed by x3 side reps with resistance band.
Prehab: Wrist strengthening - Bar, rope, weight rolls x3 /
Powerball / Tom's shoulder stabilisation exercise
Specific Strength: Sainaa 4
Alignment: Pike reps against wall / plank to pike (for fear)
Alignment: Pike against the wall taking leg off / Scissor lift to handstand
Endurance: Belly to wall endurance
Consistency: 3x sets of kicking to handstand, last one hold for 10 secs
Mobility/Flexibility: Open shoulder bar exercise

The Acrobat
Name: Rachel
Age: 20s

There are students on the other end of the fear spectrum. Meet Rachel; Rachel is a professional acrobat. She decided to make the career shift towards becoming a circus artist in her 20s and as soon as she made the decision Rachel approached it like she approaches anything: with a ferocious and fearless zeal. She trained intensively, originally as an aerialist and then internationally as a hand-to-hand flyer.

Rachel has everything. No physical limitations and a phenomenal skill level. Her progress is inspiring, she could barely touch her toes when she was 18 and now boasts a pancake flat box split.

She also has zero fear. No, really — she is limitless in her fearlessness. And this makes her a fucking good acrobat. You learn fast through fearlessness; if you have fear you will learn more slowly. Fearlessness offers scope and potential — it means you are not afraid to try. It also means you trust your body, without allowing the mind to inhibit its possibility by overthinking the action. There are limits of course, and if you forget to listen to your threat detection system altogether you are more likely to do something silly and injure yourself. I tried to trick it once and look how well that turned out.

Rachel is also off-the-wall excited by everything which means that her approach is much less methodical and a lot more hectic. If you are like Rachel and can get distracted easily, I would recommend choosing the space you train in wisely. Make sure your phone is off and that there aren't people around to distract you. You could do this by booking a space where you know you will train by yourself and coming to it with a clear objective for your session.

When Rachel and I train, we regress everything back to its basics and we do a lot of it.

Rachel's Handstand Pillars:

Specific Strength: 5/5
Endurance: 5/5
Alignment: 4/5
Consistency: 3/5
Balance: 3/5
Mobility/Flexibility: 5/5
Shape: 4/5

Rachel's Handstand Exercises:

Alignment: x3 sets handstand alignment endurance against the wall of at least 30 seconds each, focusing on the shape
Consistency: x3 sets of kicking into handstand last one hold 20 secs. Repeat x3. 10/10 exercises solo
Balance: Balance exercise
Shape: Basic shapes set (slow 10 sec hold each shape) / Lots of travelling sequences; bunny hops, straddle ups etc
Shape: Figures and shapes, transition focus. (Mexican, Scorpion, Zig-Zag, Seven)
Flexibility: Oversplit training left, right and box. Box split with wall bars and crash mat or weight on the other side x1 min per leg. Active splits, front, side and back active bar reps. Active box split reps.
Shoulders - Open shoulder bar set
Rehab: Ball rolling and STR release / Foam rolling

2. Chasing The High
BALI, OCTOBER 2015

Of all of the Hindu pantheon, it is Ganesha that I have always liked most. Not the graceful, spindly Shiva dancing in his wheel but the robust and pot-bellied elephant god. It was him who I was staring at now — seated on his throne at the front of the studio, his stony gaze staring me down.

"Don't be an asana addict," Les Leventhal's Californian cadence drifted across the room mixing lackadaisically with the sounds of enthusiastic chirping cicadas and rippling water. It was 2012 and I was in paradise, location — the Yoga Barn, Bali.

While The Yoga Barn is geographically situated in the centre of a town called Ubud, in reality it exists in another more peaceful parallel dimension — one that is much glowier, more spiritual; one where you can't walk the length of two yoga mats without someone asking for a wheatgrass shot. The Barn is dreamlike in its beauty: tiered and terraced studios emerge out of the paddy fields wrapped casually in jungle, and stone elephant trunks spout water at well-designed intervals. The impression is one of part *Avatar*, part that holiday camp from *Dirty Dancing*.

As well as hosting The Yoga Barn, Ubud, Bali is also the lush and verdant location of the last third of *Eat, Pray, Love* — one woman's pilgrimage to find herself (while eating, praying and loving). Ubud has become such a popular location for the world's yogis that a second edition is sure to be in the offing: *Eat, Juice, Yoga*. In this book we would predominantly find ourselves through eating platefuls of delicious quinoa, washing it down with a spirulina-based smoothie before heading to our mats to sun salute our troubles away.

A mosaic of these mats sprawled across The Barn's studio floor, each tile populated with a tanned, bejewelled yoga god or goddess gracefully flowing through the sequence with enviable composure. I shuffled on my mat, suddenly aware of how sweaty and red I become when I exert, not unlike a beetroot accidentally left in the sun. Of course these goddesses didn't sweat, they glowed, or at least sweated coconut water.

A ripple of laughter ran through the studio as a familiar tune started to pour from the speakers and Les reminded us that yes, Rihanna also does yoga. Clothed in Lululemon shorts and a t-shirt reading 'I'm so happy I could Kriya', Les Leventhal reminded me of a huge and gentle bear — much like the one tattooed eating out of a honeypot on his broadly muscled back (inked in honour of his first dog, Honey).

I'd heard him refer to asana 'addiction' before. I was *not* addicted to yoga poses. I mean, true that this was my third class that particular day but yoga is good for you, it *feels* good and you can't have too much of a good thing, of *yoga*, can you?

We were in pigeon, I had automatically reached back for my foot, arching my back, chin thrust forward, smile playing on my lips in expectation of that delicious tickle that means my foot had just about reached my nose. The ability to bend my spine has been folded into my DNA, daughter of a former dancer I can curl myself around as easily as spiralised courgette and, sadly, am just about as floppy.

Ganesh, remover of obstacles, stared back. His hands poised, fingers facing upwards, in *abhaya* mudra which for all intents and purposes is the international symbol of 'whoa there, easy tiger'. I paused, my back *did* feel a little achy today.

"Perhaps, just perhaps, today you don't," Les's words flowed from him, through the elephant statue and I dropped my foot. Perhaps, just perhaps, pigeon would be enough. I melted into the floor, and felt two gentle paws drawing my sacrum down.

Working in the fitness sphere, Gabby often gets asked the question "What is the best activity to get me fit and strong?" Her response is always that if you want a balanced, healthy body it is probably best to not actually specialise (at the expense of all other movement) in just one particular skill. Mix it up, dig many wells — run, do yoga, go Nordic walking, Boxercise, pick a martial art — or better, pick two!

If you *are* going to specialise in one skill though, her advice is the same as many others, be intelligent; specifically train for your activity and learn to prepare those particular muscle groups.

You are about to go for a jog; headphones are in, brand new beat-laden album cued — think Beyoncé or motivational 80s rock — 'can do' attitude amped up and a 'Just Do It' mantra buzzing through your brain. You're ready to go. You get to the park — what is the first thing you do? Maybe heft your leg up onto a tree to ease out the hamstrings, hop a little with your heel clutched towards your glute — smiling painfully at passersby?

We are meeting for a training session at The Albany, a stripped-out and echoey chapel in a graffiti-bombed side street of St Paul's. Gabby's familiarity with Bristol's burgeoning and varied practice spaces has always awed me; that month alone I had followed her to a refurbished police station, a pole studio and a former solicitor's office, all now places where people regularly meet for bending, flexing and jumping up and down.

I am a beat behind Gabby as she goes through her well-practised warm-up: swinging legs, earnest lunges, pouring weight delicately onto her spread fingers, more lunges even more earnestly. The topic of the day was how to prepare the body for exercise. Gabby is less than impressed with my amateur runner example.

She groans (not from the lunges), "I see this all of the time. Running is a dynamic activity — you want to be switching *on* your receptors, not turning them off."

I'm out of breath by the time we get to the push-ups. I grab my notebook and a towel and decide to use this as a valuable opportunity to study the acrobat in their natural habitat. And if I am to be objective, I think, probably best to write about the sit-ups rather than actually do them. I (objectively) begin to get my breath back.

"All warm ups are relative to the discipline," Gabby explains in between squat jumps. "Even in my circus school which was ahead of the curve as far as athletic training is concerned, the majority of the warm-ups were passive. You're going for a jog right? You are about to embark on a *dynamic* training session, and doing a static warm up? No way are you loading the muscle properly."

Her advice was this: next time you are about to go out for your 5km park run, instead of your usual passive stretch session prepare for a bout of explosive power by crouching as if about to start a race and then bouncing up straightening your legs. Do this prepping action a few times and see how it affects you when the whistle goes off.

So how do we relate this to our handstand preparation? Just as runners should condition with exercises that are specifically related to that sport, if you are going to spend a lot of time on your hands you obviously want to prep the hands. This preparation includes any mobilisation to get the blood into the muscle, for example by rolling the wrists or intertwining the fingers and making waves with the hands. Also gently adding weight onto the fingers. When I ask Gabby what she means by 'adding weight' she tells me that when she was at school, she did weighted wrist exercises with 10kg on her hands every morning. She never suffered a wrist injury during her training.

Wrist Strengthening Exercise

Take a bar. Tie a rope around the middle of it and attach a weight at the end. If you're on a budget and/or don't own a weight plate, grab a milk carton and fill it with rice. Start with a weight that feels comfortable for you and slowly increase it.

Holding the bar out in front of you with straight arms. Slowly start to roll the bar towards you so you are rolling the weight up. Use both wrists, rolling each one in turn: left, right, left, right.

When the weight reaches the top, reverse the process by rolling it back down. Try and keep the arms as straight as possible at all times so the exercise can really target the muscles in the wrists.

Repeat x5

For those in the athletically professional sphere however one particular part of the body does unavoidably tend to get a pummelling; whether you're a runner and your knees get shot, a ballerina and your hips start to crunch or an incessant writer trapped in an ironic loop of journalling others' handstands whose wrists start to feel the ache of repetitive strain…

We should of course listen to our bodies' pleadings for balance, but we are creatures of glorious habit and addiction, and so the pummelling, crunching and straining continues until some of us luckier ones limp and hobble into our physio's office or the more plucky into the local yoga studio and demand our bodies to be put back together, piece by pummelled piece.

Handstands, if social media is to be believed, have for the wellness world turned into an obsession. For an industry so concerned with life's balance, this is a pose (albeit a balance-y one) that we just can't get enough of — a desire has been tapped and the flood is seemingly unending.

My first call regarding this desire is to Les, my first teacher to call me on my asana addiction and one as famous for his checkered past as for his electric teaching style. My first question — what did he used to be addicted to?

"Methamphetamine, cocaine, pot, Ecstasy, Ketamine, Valium, Halcion, Ativan, alcohol, shopping, sex, food."

"Huh. What food?" I ask.

"Specifically Krispy Kreme donuts. Oh, and later, yoga."

If ever there was a rockstar yogi, Les is it. We were talking
via the wonders of the inter-web; Les had just touched
down in Beirut, had just arrived from Prague and was
about to leave back to Bali for another round of teacher
trainings. This recent schedule, while hectic, is not overly
unusual for him. Les is of the new brand of yoga
headliners. No longer teaching regular classes he instead
teaches workshops to packed out studios and is sought out
at festivals where 250 plus yogis, hearts beating and
ponytails swishing, practise in gleeful unison to Les's
playful playlist and soak up every nugget of his hard-
earned wisdom. Much of this wisdom is documented in
his page-turning autobiography, soon hopefully to be made
into a film: *Two Lifestyles, One Lifetime. An Inspiring Journey
from Rock-Bottom Hopelessness to Wildly Extravagant Possibility.*

Les's rock bottom was rockier than most. At 17 he was
already walking the path of the addict, abusing alcohol
and addicted to crystal-meth. At 16 he'd had enough of
living in the small towns of Seaford, New York and
Indianapolis, Indiana (splitting time between his mom and
dad) and using his stepdad's credit card he bought a flight
to Los Angeles, leaving with nothing but $28 and, back
then (Les is now gloriously bald), lots of hair products and
an ill-conceived idea of becoming rich, fit and/or famous.
Once there, in desperate need of food and shelter, he
turned to prostitution.

Les fought hard to find his way into recovery, living 21
years in San Francisco, finally getting a job at a bank
leasing aircraft engines to South American Airlines. He
was not looking for yoga. He was an addict in recovery, a
banker and full-time gym bunny, he (he confesses) didn't
have the time: "I would get in the gym at 5 or 5.30am,

121

smash out some weights, run to the shower, run to work…
I was always running."

He would look through the glass at the people practising
yoga in the gym; they dressed differently, they moved
differently, they were most certainly *not* his people. It was
his weightlifting buddy who suggested that with all the
weights they were pulling, they might you know, want to
stretch once in a while.

Les remembers his first yoga session on the gym's grubby
mats, in the uninspiring room, doing what he thought at
the time was a bunch of ridiculous postures. "I thought,
this is *so* not for me." And then they laid down for *savasana*.

The tears came quick and fast. Huge, surprisingly visceral,
waves of surrender and release washed over him. He
couldn't believe it, he also didn't want to admit it —
rubbing the tears away frantically in case any of his gym
comrades were themselves gazing in, looking at all of these
weirdly dressed people doing yoga instead of lifting
weights lying on the floor, and look one of them is *crying!*

He'd had his first taste of yoga — the high, the connection
— after all this time maybe this is what he'd been looking
for from the drugs and alcohol, except this time he could
(legally) drive home afterwards.

Les continued doing yoga at the gym until one morning he
was lining up to get his habitual double espresso from
Peet's Coffee in downtown San Francisco, his new (less
grubby) yoga mat strapped to his back. A guy tapped him
on the shoulder. "Do you practise?" he asked. Les stared at
him, not yet familiar with yoga-speak, "Er, practise what?"
This guy was Rusty Wells, now world-renowned, then

teacher at the popular studio YogaTree where Les would eventually become one of the senior instructors.

Les became a converted regular at Rusty's popular Bhakti Yoga class on a Sunday morning. They would chant, they would sweat and they would dance through their poses to music from the Black Eyed Peas to Bill Withers. At this point Les was still heavily into the gay party scene and of course, the party the night before was affecting the practice the morning after.

After a few months, Rusty asked him what he did on a Saturday night. "I go out," Les replied, as if, well of course I go out and then I get up and I struggle through class and while the other yogis go to breakfast together, I struggle straight out the door, into my car and home.

Gently, Rusty probed. "Have you ever thought of, perhaps, not?" Les paused. "Maybe you do dinner and a movie with Joe, and then maybe, just maybe, you don't go to a club afterwards?"

This idea of not doing everything is increasingly alien to our modern sensibility. When everything is available, how can we just take a little? If our bodies are able to do this, why would we not ask them to? If I *can* put my foot on my head, why would I not? The hashtag 'yoga every damn day' haunts my social media feeds and seems to be a symptom of this understandable excitement surrounding our bodies' new found possibilities. How about instead the rather less flashy 'yoga every now and then'? The ability to say no sometimes (to chocolate, to the 'next episode' button on Netflix, to the colleague with offerings of extra work and yes, even to yoga) is also a muscle worth stretching.

The truth that we are able to stop before we are forced to, whether by the snap of a hamstring, a crumbling relationship or the debilitating collapse of the adrenals due to stress, is for many of us a revelation. This body wisdom is evolved slowly: to take a little, not everything; to give some, not all.

When I see Ganesha now, unblinking, palm towards me with his heavy feet steadfastly planted on the earth, he is showing me how to take a stand. He is the remover of obstacles, sometimes these obstacles are physical and their removal will allow us to move more easily into a pose but more often the thing that needs to be removed (or at least tempered) is desire for the pose in the first place.

Life as an international yoga teacher can be demanding; long haul flights, intensive training months where Les wakes at 4 and arrives on the mat at 5.30am ready to practise before he teaches and guides the future instructors in their spiritual and physical journeys. How does he keep his balance on this rollercoaster ride?

"Over time, I've learned when to say no when I know I need rest and to let people know that I'm in training and I need a day off… I cannot be of service to others if I am not allowing myself to be spiritually fed. I'm not your Instagram, get the handstand moment, kind of teacher. I love these teachers and I love the gifts that so many of them have. Rather my work is teaching what I'm working on: trauma, abuse, attempted suicide and addiction. I know that I attract that… So, I need that Zumba class, longer meditation, ice cream, sunrise, sunset and massage."

Les quit the bank in 2005. Not thinking he wanted to teach, but knowing that he wanted to keep practising, after much stalling he took the leap and stepped into his yoga teacher training with Ana Forrest. One week in he had made up his mind; he was going to teach. He made the phone call to Yoga Tree in the car on the way home to San Francisco. He'd heard no one wanted to cover the early morning teaching slots; the years of sales paid off and he started work as a yoga teacher in one of the most popular studios in the city just the next week. As his classes filled, he was soon offered the more prized, and busier, afternoon time slots.

"I used to teach Friday 4:30 at the Tree and once all 100 people finally got in, usually about 4:40pm, we needed to chant — so it was everyone to the wall — Handstand and 3 *Oms*. Book back to the mat and chair pose and off we went. For me, I don't mind rolling the mat out and *poof!* Forearm balance! I do like my inversions at the front of the practice, not the back end. Inversions for me are like those energiser drinks or a quad chai latte (dirty of course). They supercharge my energy. So, when I'm about to teach at a yoga festival and there's 250+ people on the mats, right before I teach, you will find me very well warmed up from a practice and doing one last handstand."

Les's workshops are often based around the chakras, the seven sacred coloured clusters yogis believe to be a map of a person's energy. Handstands and arm balances for Les are third chakra poses, this third centre is associated with tribe and personal power.

"We already know that I broke a lot (ok, *all*) of the rules my parents laid out for me… but breaking the laws of the universe, defying gravity in search of what else is really out there beside this teeny tiny one little Earth ball? Now *that* is sexy."

The allure of handstands suddenly crystallised for me; they were the leather-jacketed James Dean lookalike that rolled up to your parents' house in a battered convertible. They were rebellious, a little dangerous, and set your heart racing.

They *were* sexy.

Les continued, "The fire of third chakra is part of me growing up, being a more responsible adult and *harnessing* all that energy that I would let flail around in ways that were never helpful or useful for anyone. Now I have practices to gift and guide. That feels amazing to be able to take so much of my past struggles and see how that can help people heal and possibly even save lives. *That* is shifting perspective and turning things upside down."

At 64, Gabby's mum Sara is just starting to learn to go upside down. After years of trying to convince her to give handstanding a go, Gabby brought Sara to my yoga class. Yoga seemed an innocuous enough request after all. An hour and 15 minutes in and it was time for an inversion. We were doing the scissor lift exercise (p32) into handstands and Sara decided absolutely that she couldn't do it. Reminding her that she was the mother of a handstand teacher, Gabby was having none of this and hoisted her mum physically into position. Finding balance for just the briefest of moments, Sara came down almost straight away — her face beaming the bright slightly shocked smile of someone unlocking a forgotten vine-covered door and finding a blooming garden inside. Once discovered you knew it had always been there.

We hear stories of professionals only finding their true calling late in life; Andrea Bocelli used to be a lawyer, Sylvester Stallone was a lion cage cleaner and Walt Disney was a newspaper editor (before being fired for not having enough 'good ideas'). The same can be said of accessing new ways to move physically. Ambra Vallo (or 'Ambrasana'), a yogi who has the jaw-dropping muscular physicality of Lynda Carter as Wonder Woman (if Lynda was blonder and quite a bit bendier) only came to the mat after retiring from a career as the prima ballerina of the Birmingham Royal Ballet at 41 years old.

"I started yoga and I couldn't even do half a *chaturanga*; my ballerina legs were strong but I had absolutely *no* strength in my arms." Ambra is now known as one of the strongest practitioners in the industry, regularly running workshops on how to float and fly on the mat and is also, incidentally, the yoga teacher to the Aston Villa football team.

Inversions demand that you harness your *inner* as well as outer strength, even strength you didn't know you had, like Gabby's mum. Sara is stronger than she thought, she is so strong in fact that she is able to hold herself upside down on her arms — which is an incredibly empowering thing to do!

While my handstands still tend to start with a little prayer ('please all-powerful inversion gods, if I do smush my face, please let no one be filming it'), eventually after enough practice we are no longer moving into the unknown by going upside down but accessing strength and skill that we have trained, we understand and know well. We are finally able to look these sexy handstands in the eye, pull on our

own leather jackets, push them into the passenger's seat
and tell them that it's 'my turn to drive, actually'.

Having turned his world upside down and right side up,
Les is now 16 years sober, sporting his recovery medallion
proudly on all social media platforms; a trophy of his own
strength, discipline and dedication to his path. Now on the
days that he's not yoga-ing (and even on some of those)
you'll find him at the local Zumba class, back in the gym
lifting weights or on his two treat days a week (more if
husband Joe has anything to say about it) chasing the
dream of eating coconut ice cream out of real coconuts.

Rock bottom to rockstar yogi looks pretty good from here.

The Construction Manager
Name: Darren
Age: 50s

Darren has lived life. He explains the heart surgery and hip replacement as easily as he discusses his passion for dancing, football and boxing. His background in movement was apparent as soon as we started lessons, a keen listener he learns fast — his lean sinewy frame adapting as easily to being upside down as it does to salsa or the chacha.

Within two sessions I could see a marked improvement, which is unusual even for a physically capable student. Curious, I ask how much he is training. "Sundays are my rest days" he replies. He leads a balanced life; he is calm; he has forged a strong connection between his mind and body, his mindset is on point and it is this, rather than his sporty background, that is allowing him to progress so quickly.

Initially he started training handstands by himself, using some online videos, but soon saw that he wasn't making any progress. Darren is so wonderfully unique because he has accepted that it will take time, he never books just one session but 8 or even 12. For him handstands are a journey to a skill rather than a get-sick-trick-quick kind of deal.

Darren is a lover of all things fitness and health related, because of this I tend to explain exercises in greater geeky detail than I usually would with a client. Darren has a very physical job working in construction, and has bucket loads of strength coupled with a hyper-trophied upper body. It will take longer for Darren to access this shape due to the fact that he does not have much experience within this particular discipline, however he doesn't lack specific strength. The things holding him back on maintaining a straight handstand for 10 seconds are mainly consistency and balance. He will need balance techniques introduced into his body so that he can stop balancing the handstand with different body parts (e.g. moving the legs over the back

and compensating by moving the shoulders). *Eventually he will learn
to only use his fingers and hands. These are the missing links in
Darren's ability to hold a handstand.*

Darren's Handstand Pillars

*Specific Strength: 3/5
Endurance: 3/5
Alignment: 3/5
Consistency: 3/5
Balance: 2/5
Mobility/Flexibility: 2/5
Shape: 1/5*

Darren's Handstand Exercises

*Specific strength: Sainaa 4 / Plank to pike reps x3x3
Alignment: 3 Positions Against Wall / Pike reps
Endurance: 3x30 secs endurance position against the wall with shape
focus
Consistency: Level up Consistency Exercise with 10 opportunities to
hold each repetition for 10 secs
Balance: Balance Exercise x 3
Shape: Basic Shape Set (x10 secs per shape) / Variation of entrances
into handstand / travelling sequences
Mobility / Flexibility: Open shoulder bar stretch / Chair partner
stretch*

Do not confuse motion and progress.
A rocking horse keeps moving but does not make any progress

— Alfred A. Montapert

3. Breathe If You Want To Go Faster

Have you ever played the game 'Spoons'? The basic
setup (and I'm sure there are many variations) is that some
spoons are placed in the middle of a circle, one less than
there are players. Cards are dealt and in a flurry of passing
cards to the left you try to be the first one to get a
matching set. If you are the first person to get four
matching cards you surreptitiously take one of the spoons,
sneakily removing it from the centre — slipping it into

your sleeve or under a foot. As soon as another player notices, there is a scramble (and often a wrestling match) to not be the one player left spoonless.

Now imagine this game but instead of spoons you use wet floor signs, and these wet floor signs are not placed in the middle of the players but scattered around a college campus. Imagine the chaos caused by a dozen skidding teenagers across slippery floors and then imagine the person who would orchestrate such a crazy game: athletic, exhaustingly energetic and infamously difficult to pin down — meet my best friend Will.

Given these innate character traits, it has always been understandably difficult to nudge, beg and beguile Will towards any kind of static activity, even (and perhaps especially) my yoga classes.

Will felt a wariness towards yoga. As if by asking him to invest in a mat and stretchy shorts I was instead demanding he make a deal with a mischievous and mercurial pixie. Yes, (the yoga pixie would promise) he would be able to place his palms neatly on the floor when folding forward but as a surprising and hilarious addition he would also start spouting Sanskrit and affecting a need for £5 bottles of coconut water. This was an idea that I found ridiculous, and told him so.

In the end it took my sister-in-law, Mel, inviting us both to her favourite New York yoga studio that swung it. "Keith is teaching," she said, all Bambi eyes and dreamy expression, "you'll just love him, and the yoga."

Like most other chic New Yorkers, Mel has integrated yoga into her everyday life in the same way as your average Briton might the gym. Even if you don't go every week, you know it's there, you know it's good for you and you know there's a place you can go do it right around the corner. Walking down the city's sidewalks a yogi/yogini with a mat strapped to his/her back is as typical and expected a sighting as a yellow cab.

Entering through an unobtrusive poster-splattered door on 54th Street, we arrived 20 minutes early to be assured a good mat-space. NYC studios — stylish havens for the city's beautiful people. I inhaled. This is the place, this is where yoga clichés were packaged up, slapped on the cover of Yoga Journal and shipped out into the rest of the world. Compare these groovy shalas with the standard West Country community hall, the sole decorative feature being one dusty aloe vera plant shoved in the corner, and you might be nearing the reason why British yoga has taken a lot longer to acquire the 'cool' it wears in America so casually.

It is happening though. Students wanting to fuse a workout, a rave and a stretch coupled with a light dose of spiritual therapy are flooding into classes that promise to tick all of the boxes and as a bonus, kick your butt (and tone it too). The British Yoga Constabulary stand gulping at the gates as the sexy new Lycra-ed brand of yoga storms the UK yoga scene (and looks fabulous doing it).

Long ago in a desert far far away, before Lycra had even been invented, lived Pashupati. Pashupati is a squat, inscrutable figure who sits carved in meditation and while he is smaller than a postage stamp his role in the history of yoga looms large. He is the first image (that we know of) of a yogi. Pashupati 'lord of the animals' is the original yoga poster pin-up.

Skip forward four and a half millennia, after Mahatma Gandhi (a yogi) and before Mountbatten (not a yogi, as far as we know) and traditional Indian postural yoga was becoming over-shadowed by a wave of bodybuilding and British gymnastics.

It was 1931 and T. Krishnamacharya had just been hired by the Maharaja of Mysore. His brief was to create a rigorous and intelligent yoga asana programme for the royal boys at the palace. Traditional Hatha (physical) yoga was originally developed to create ease in the body when meditating but these lads didn't need to sit, they needed to move; the Maharaja wanted them strong, supple and suitably disciplined for soldiering.

Krishnamacharya must have done a good job because just two years later the Maharaja was building him an entirely new wing of the palace to use as his very own yoga shala.

It was at this time that Krishnamacharya began developing the *surya namaskar* (salute to the sun). Part of this sequence, the 'vinyasa', is now used in many yoga classes as the linking movement between postures. A vinyasa consists of a plank, *chaturanga dandasana* (bottom bit of a push-up), an *urdva mukhasana* or upward-facing dog (a backbend with only tops of the feet and palms on the floor) and a downward-facing dog. Krishnamacharya's *surya namaskar* would be taken up by his pupil K. Pattabhi Jois (*guruji* to Kino MacGregor and thousands of others), the creator of the Ashtanga Vinyasa method.

In the early 1980s Larry Schultz was enjoying Happy Hour in a bar in Jamaica. Looking out over the beach towards the crystal clear ocean he saw a man balancing on a rock, doing what at the time to him looked liked Tai Chi or some kind of meditative dance. Larry was entranced, but also sadly drunk and passed out before he could ask the Tai Chi dancer what he was up to.

The next day he saw the man again, and eager not to miss his chance he sped up to him, "What was is it you were doing, yesterday on that rock? I watched you; you didn't stop moving for more than two whole hours."

The man replied, "I was doing yoga."

Larry probed further, "What kind of yoga?"

"Ashtanga Yoga."

"Hmm," Larry looked the man up and down. "Ashtanga Yoga. How old are you?'

The man, unperturbed at the questioning responded, "I'm 63."

"63? You look beautiful for 63!" Looking over the man's shoulder, Larry nodded to the woman behind him. "Who's that?"

"That's my girlfriend."

"How old is she?"

"She's 23."

Huh, Larry thought, I gotta get me some of that 'Ashtanga Yoga'. A couple of years later Larry was in Mysore practising this Ashtanga with Pattabhi Jois himself.

The Ashtanga method consists of set sequences, six series of postures each more advanced than the one before. It is traditionally practised 'Mysore style' where each student does their own practice in a group setting while being checked and adjusted by a teacher; the student is only allowed to advance to the next pose when having mastered the previous one. Fine if you have the lean and athletic somatotype of some of the Ashtanga godfathers such as Tim Miller or David Swenson, not so fine if you are a slightly bulkier Jewish Texan. While having the deepest of respect for his teachers and to the lineage they represented, Larry decided to go rogue.

A few years later, Larry landed the gig of touring with the Grateful Dead as their yoga teacher. Bob Weir, their lead guitarist, had decided that the practice Larry was teaching them needed a name.

"Rocket Yoga?"

Larry asked, "Why Rocket Yoga?'

Bob replied simply, "Because it gets you there faster."

Vinyasa Flow, Power Yoga, Dynamic Vinyasa, Prana Flow, the fabulous Rocket Yoga — these are all creative offshoots of Krishnamacharya and Jois's series of flowing postures.

Most are fast-paced, intricately sequenced and often practised to music. It is in this style of yoga class in particular that more and more complex postures can be added and these exciting and elusive handstand variations can be scattered liberally — dangling like acrobatic carrots in front of eager athletic practitioners. Flow, invert, rinse, repeat.

90 minutes later we emerged from Keith's Vinyasa class doused in incense and glistening with a sheen of smugness and sweat. Energetic, filled with challenge, a feeling of having worked (and worked hard) — this was a yoga Will's frenetically active system could understand. Two days later and considerably more dollars lighter we left Lululemon, Will carrying his very first Yoga mat, slung casually over his shoulder like a proper New York yogi.

Every other person I have asked (and I have asked a lot), "Why are handstands so popular in yoga?" has answered, "It's a trend."

The trend is body beautiful. The trend is fitness. The trend is to move and to move fast. Yoga, any studio owner will tell you, is on trend. It is tempting to see yoga and its many branches as having a bit of a crisis of identity: it is meditative and yet at the same time fast-paced; it celebrates the beautiful body and yet also seeks to calm the inner landscape of the mind. Yoga has hit its mid-life, has seen the world moving on without it and thought 'fuck it, I'm buying a sports car'.

Yoga is competing in a market filled with new ways to move, to get fit and to get strong. While many of us now spend an equal amount of time on Mac as on mat attempting to drum up students to fill our classes, there are some who seem to attract attention in the same way as they lift into a handstand — with enviable ease (a clever disguise no doubt for the effort behind the social media magnet and handstanding machine). Patrick Beach is one of these people.

An Instagram account filled in equal parts with balances, wistful gazes and puppy dogs has led Patrick to an astounding 349,000 followers. In turn this has manifested into sold out studios across the globe and ranks of yogis and yoginis practising with him online, occasionally looking up from their third or fourth core exercise to gaze as he gracefully floats from balance to handstand, still guiding them through with his trippingly lilting twang.

Will, fresh from his New York Vinyasa experience and still sporting his new mat, and I had arrived half an hour early to Patrick's workshop. Thinking we would be seen as a little keen, we dawdled lazily from Marylebone tube station to Indaba Yoga chatting about what new variations, revelations or techniques would be gifted to us in the next three hours. We entered the studio to a tsunami of towels, trainers and tasteful tattoos.

Yoga's love affair with arm balances was well-represented, with almost 90 mats filled with handstand-hungry students. I scanned the room — a guy to the left of me was taking a selfie (a shirtsie?) of his t-shirt which had the words 'Real Men Do Yoga' emblazoned across it; he kept looking around excitedly as if making sure that everyone else was just as thrilled to be there as he was.

I gave him a smile back, assuring myself as well as him that yes this was going to be an exciting workshop and no I wasn't terrified at all. A girl two mats in front was casually describing her history with handstands to her neighbour, "Yeah, I mean one time in fifty I hit the balance perfectly." I nodded out of view, my head bouncing up and down like one of those plastic dogs on a car dashboard. She, this yoga Amazon — all golden muscles and jingling anklets — was one of my people, the people who tried.

Her equally Amazonian neighbour's eyes flicked between her and the studio door where any moment, Patrick would emerge.

My new handstand ally continued hopefully, unaware of her friend's waning interest "…but soon it will be one in 40, then one in 30, then…"

"Elusivity," Patrick told me when I, yoga-stoned and sweaty, caught him afterwards. In one word, this to him was the magic of handstands. "Not everyone can access deep hip opening," he murmured his wisdom through his fantastic beard.

"Not everyone can access deep backbends but *everyone* can access handstands…" my heart leapt, backflipping with joy — hear that? Everyone can handstand! "…With enough effort." My heart sank, realising that it in fact couldn't actually do a backflip and should probably stop before it hurts itself.

"I'm even teaching my 65-year-old mum to handstand," he grinned and backtracked charmingly, "No wait, she's 60, she's actually 60."

The Aerialist
Name: Sudhira
Age: 40s

We begin our life's journey crawling and exploring the ground with our palms. Many of us handstand all the time as children but as adults something shifts. There is now so much fluff in the way — it could be fear of injury, or just the cumulative years of seeing the world the 'right' way up.

Meet Sudhira — a circus artist, proofreader, piano tuner and meditator. As an aerialist, Sudhira came to me to help her integrate handstands into her creative pieces; floor work was something she wanted to develop and she had a love of handbalancing — finding equal grace in movements on the ground as in the air.

Sudhira is a fabulous example of someone that started learning this skill later in life, starting to train circus at the age of 39.

I don't have favourites, but if I did Sudhira would be one of them. She is calm, patient, dedicated, wise and beautiful inside and out. I remember going to watch her final piece after she graduated her degree in circus and performance arts. I felt like a proud mum, even though she's 10 years my senior. She has trained with me twice a week for over two years and in that time I've seen her transform from handstand newbie into handstand demi goddess.

I remember that we'd gone to London together for a workshop with handbalancer Nico. Returning the next day I was hung over and a little groggy (post post-handstanding festivities), getting in the car I noticed that Sudhira had a picture on her dashboard of a man, a warm smile shining out from his tanned face. I asked her who he was and Sudhira told me it was her meditation teacher from New York. She apologised and told me that she had to do a "little minute" of meditation every time she got into the car before she started to drive. It was a beautiful thing to witness.

This reflective nature is also typical of Sudhira's approach to her training, going through the steps methodically with a slow, steady pace. She is experiential and has a deep relationship with movement and through her performance art she is able to key into this mind-body connection in order to create something entirely unique.

Sudhira's approach is perfect for her, but it is slow. In order to progress fast, handstands demand that you obsess over them. Lukewarm sentiment just doesn't cut it. Of course you can flirt with handstands, but ultimately they will only truly be yours if you eventually get the guts to grab them by the shoulders and give them a sloppy wet kiss on the mouth.

Sudhira's relationship with handstands is this gentle flirtation, my job as her teacher is to fan the flames into a wild and passionate affair; I've found that by building up the difficulty throughout the session, we are half way through before she notices that she's working as hard as she is! And she does work really hard.

Everyone builds their energy differently. When I was training pole dance I would put on gloriously loud music to get me into the spirit of the practice. You could also make yourself warmer physically in the body so that you feel more ready to move — jumping around to this same music in a cosy hoody works just as well! It could be that your motivation is kindled by watching an inspiring video, I have a friend who reads a chapter of an inspiring book before she starts to work — at the moment she is reading What The Most Successful People Do Before Breakfast *before she eats breakfast. Everyone will find their own path but fables aside, whilst the tortoise may be the wiser traveller it is the hare that will ultimately get there (and get upside down) faster.*

Sudhira's Handstand Pillars

Specific Strength: 4/5
Endurance: 3/5
Alignment: 4/5
Consistency: 3/5
Balance: 3/5
Mobility/Flexibility: 4/5
Shape: 4/5

Sudhira's Handstand Exercises

Alignment: Pike reps x3 sets of 10 secs, repeat x3
Endurance: 3x 30 secs against the wall / 3 position against the wall
/ Push&Pull exercise for stacking weight failure resistance
Consistency: Consistency exercise with hand and head variation /
10/10 exercise with lower back spotting or solo
Balance: Balance Exercise x3
Shape: Basic Shape Set (x10 secs per shape)
Shape: Figures and shapes (mexican, scoprion, zig-zag, Seven)
Mobility/Flexibility: Box split resistance band x2 mins + active
reps. Oversplit + active split reps / Shoulders: Open shoulders bar
exercise + rotator cuff stretches (vogue stretch)
Rehab: Ball rolling + STR release / Foam rolling / Shoulder
prehab

Do your practice and all is coming

– K. Pattabhi Jois

4. The Work

"He's over for a few weeks from Montréal," Gabby explained over the phone. "An old friend from circus school. Would you mind an extra mouth to feed?" And then adding quickly, "we'll bring wine."

A few hours and quite a few glasses later…

"I'm *not* saying I'm not short." — Gabby.

"Good, because you really really are." (Me, I'm 5'2" on a tall day, and this was, I should stress, said with love).

"I'm just saying that I'm not *really* short. I mean, there are people shorter."

"Like who?"

"Like Oompa Loompas?" Will calls in from the kitchen where he's been washing up and apparently eavesdropping.

"I'm *not* an Oompa Loompa… I'm slightly taller, I looked it up."

The dinner party had been designed as a quiet and humble house-warming. I'd cooked curry; cycled to Ikea for extra cutlery; begged, borrowed and stolen you'd-hardly-notice-it's-not-matching crockery and even found the perfect selection of paperbacks (not too pretentious, quite quirky, mostly Penguins) to stack as what I considered to be a charming Pinterest-worthy centre piece.

It looked beautiful. For around 45 minutes. It was now 9pm and all pretence of grown-uppery, Penguin Classics included, had been pushed to the side along with the dinner table (that was in reality one part table, two parts desk).

This was the night that I found out what happens when you get more than one acrobat in a room together and feed them alcohol. The answer? Handstands. Handstands happen.

RULES TO THE HANDSTAND GAME
(*do* try this at home)

1.   There *must* be two people handstanding at any one time. If there aren't, the game is over and you have all won.

2.   When you are about to come down from your handstand, shout "I'M COMING DOWN" (or, if you are Gabrielle Parker, "aaaaaaargh, this is *so* SO stressful").

3.   If you are Gabrielle Parker's friend Reuben Hosler and can stay on two arms forever, do this in a one-armed handstand. Just to make it fair.

I have only spent a couple of winters in the UK since university and every year I forget how luxuriantly and petrifyingly icy they are. I have been known to wear two pairs of gloves, recently using the new high-tech iPhone friendly ones over the top in order to sate the ever-present seasonal tick of looking up Skyscanner flights to India, Bali or Ibiza.

Warm fires, hot chocolates, bonfires in unlikely places and long, sweaty indoor training sessions are all apparently part of what makes a Bristol January. We'd been invited on one of these famous training sessions by our friend Jane and temporarily forgetting about the arctic conditions with promises of pasta at hers afterwards, I had agreed to travel there on the back of Will's motorbike.

Reaching the Kingswood gym we were welcomed by enthusiastic waves from the collected acrobats, at a glance I saw Sudhira, Rachel and Gabby all midway through performing something wildly complicated. I did wave back in response but because I still couldn't move my freezing fingers, the wave looked less enthusiastic and more like the ones the Queen gives out of her carriage window at ceremonial parades.

As I started to jump up and down on the spot, stubbornly refusing to take off any layers, I used the time to survey the many professionals going about their training. In the middle of the gym our friend Richard was holding the lunge system while Rachel bounced, gleefully somersaulting between bases — forwards and then, after encouraging cheers of "link it, link it!", also backwards.

"Yeehaa!" She unhooked the harness, hugged Rich, high-fived her spotters and waved at us, peroxide pigtails bouncing.

Gabby was at the far end, half a dozen encouraging onlookers grouped around her watching her gurn and swear through trying a standing one-armed long-arm (hand-to-hand) for the first time in about five years.

Amidst this cheery crowd I recognised Reuben, calmly pressing upside down on handstand canes before levering silently to the ground; feline in his grace, grin and nonchalance. It was like watching a concert pianist practise his scales; no applause or fuss, just elegant in their simplicity, ego-less and full of beauty.

Somewhere between the curry and the one-armed handstands I had somehow corralled Reuben into giving me a Skype interview. It was my first official-ish acrobat chat over the web and I wanted to be prepared. I'd drafted some questions, spent the morning Googling and realised what I wanted to know was not why, but more particularly, how Reuben had found such ease in handstands. Much to my surprise given what I'd seen in the gym, Gabby had told me that Reuben no longer performs; I wanted to ask him about that too.

My notepad and pen poised, I clicked the big blue 'S' icon.

It rang.

"Hello, Reuben?"

Silence.

Reuben's face appeared and he appeared to be mouthing words, but with no sound. Damn it. The microphone wasn't working. We interpretive-danced our way through to a different method of online communication.

Ugh. I un-clicked my special note-taking pen and leant back in my chair. "Oh f —"

"Ash?"

"Er, Reuben? Hi!"

As the Facebook chat icon pinged on, Reuben materialised on screen in his other (perhaps less glamorous) guise as owner of 'Reuben Hosler SEO'.

I made a joke about him having two identities, at which point he pulled on a Batman mask which (for some reason) he'd brought with him to his new 'super serious' place of work.

Batman as a superhero does not have an easy time of it physically, just like the old-school heroes of Greek myth he is *super* human but he is also super *human*. We see Batman bleed, break bones, in the last film he even walks with a cane, hobbling grumpily and stoically around Wayne Manor. And with all of these impingements he still performs incredible feats of athleticism. Every hero has an Achilles Heel, and in Batman's case he has about a dozen.

Reuben's Achilles Heel, it turns out, is his shoulder.

A woman walked past the window of Reuben's office and catching sight of him in his Batman mask doubled-back, blinking. Reuben had by then taken it off, lightning fast.

"I have a tendency to be quite relaxed in the joints," Reuben smiled.

Yes, his shoulder is so relaxed in fact that it likes to take a vacation now and again from its socket and say, flop out — all relaxed. It happened once at circus school, mid double-back somersault on a trampoline. Reuben landed clutching his arm. It happened again, this time on stage where he was flying on a *banquine* platform, where the bases' wrists form a lattice that you jump off. Reuben missed this platform, managing to slow himself down by absorbing some of the weight on his arm. This time his shoulder popped out long enough for his friend to ask "Are you ok?" and Reuben to reply, "No, no I'm not." He didn't stop flying though; three weeks later he was performing again and carried on for another year and a half in professional circus.

But now it was holiday time, and Reuben was ready to hit the slopes. Most coaches ban their performers from winter sports, or in fact any sports that might end up with their acrobats' valuable limbs being in any way damaged. Reuben being the charmer that he is and his coach being of the kinder sort, January 2015 was an exception.

Days of risky and exhilarating snowboarding passed incident-free, that is until the last day.

There had been enough risk and it was the last, much safer pass before home. Reuben was coasting along when he caught the front of his board in the snow and shoulder-barged the slope.

"It felt like being punched in the deltoid muscle by someone huge. Punched hard."

He knew something was wrong straight away, unlike his shoulder's former flakiness this time he could feel things moving which shouldn't have been moving. He had torn his labrum everywhere — the front, the top and a bit at the back and torn the ligaments connecting the shoulder to the collar bone. His circus Achilles Heel had snapped.

So far Reuben has managed to avoid surgery, though it's still on the cards. Working intensively with his physio, at one point he was spending 12 hours a week at the gym working on his atrophied teres minor and trying to build up muscle bulk to support the shoulder joint. Movements such as throwing a ball, playing table tennis — anything with rapid, wide-arching movement of the shoulder — shift Reuben's rehabilitation into the danger zone and both he and his shoulder have to back off. Trampoline is very risky, as is basing trapeze.

He can still handstand though.

Reuben is uncannily stoic about his injury. "It was a necessary evil," he shrugs, fingers grazing nervously through thick McDreamy style waves of black hair. "For life, for what I wanted overall from life. Now I can separate circus from money, and that's a better way for me to be. That way circus can be more about the enjoyment." He pauses, "Rather than being forced to risk your life for money you can risk it for fun instead."

Reuben still coaches circus, whenever he's in the country he is Gabby's first call for private handstand tuition; he works with the Acroyogis in Montréal, helping them move through their handstand transitions with increasing grace; he guides hand-to-hand artists into higher and more refined feats of technical flight.

Genius is 1% inspiration, 99% perspiration

— Thomas Edison

There was a study which brought a thousand International Masters and Grandmasters together. They all had studied 10,000 hours or more of chess and were at the very top of their game (their game of course being chess). The difference between them however, that which separated the 'very good' from 'the very best' was that while the International Masters spent 10% of their practice time studying strategy and learning theory, the Grandmasters continued to spend at least half of their time swotting up, and only 50% on playing the game itself. That is 50% of their time reading and studying the theory of their chosen skill.

I had been asking "how do you get good at handstands?" The reference to pretty much the most static pastime I could think of (bar perhaps, internet chess) confused me. Reuben assured me that the same intelligent training philosophy applied to handstands, the certain truth that it is actually (in Reuben's words) "all of the crap, boring bits of practice that make you really good at what you do."

"This is the system of the National Circus School in Montréal. They have the best coaches (Russian, obviously) and the most insane handbalancers. Each session however starts off with the same exercises. You start on two hands, going through a series of shapes. Then the blocks come out and you walk on your hands from block to block going through your different handstand shapes. I've met an acrobat there that can balance a handstand for seven minutes, another that can spend 13 minutes swopping from one arm to the other. These are handstand masters, but even when they leave circus school they will begin their practice the same way — they will start out on two hands, and then they will get their blocks out. It's not that there's not ego, they just understand that to get that good you practise your basics, your theory."

As with most circus arts, Reuben explains, handstands require a decent amount of dedication and the ability to suffer. There are of course, different kinds (and different degrees) of suffering. You will meet contortionists (some, not all) who discuss a 'breaking through of the pain threshold'; in acrobatics — you fall, you say "fuck, that hurts," you carry on. Handstands however are more akin to juggling: the daily grind of repetition, the constant understanding that you will continue to spend an unfair amount of time doing the same thing, over and over and over and over. Plus, your muscles hurt. A lot.

80% of success is just showing up

— Woody Allen

"Handstands are fun, but handstand training to actually improve is, basically, boring. I didn't realise this at first. When my hand-to-hand base started training a lot more with his girlfriend I thought I'd just switch, you know, get good at handstands. I booked two hours in the training space but after 25 minutes I'd practised all of the shapes I wanted to, all of the fun stuff and thought 'well, this is boring' and left. Unfortunately it is the efficient and intelligent training — basically all of the crap bits of practice — that make you really good."

Haruki Murakami in his book *What I Talk About When I Talk About Running* quotes Somerset Maugham and his insight that 'in each shave lies a philosophy'. Murakami writes that 'no matter how mundane an action might appear, keep at it long enough and it becomes a contemplative, even meditative act'.

Brushing your teeth for example, or taking your morning jog, perhaps even flowing through a sun salutation — those same movements become ingrained in our muscles like water wearing at stone; these actions that we do daily

have the capacity to become habit-driven repetitions of
the same action. Brush up, brush down; one foot in front
of the other, turn left at the postbox; inhale reach up,
exhale hands to *Namaste*.

To take an example, if we were to compare a 17-year-old
with a 45-year-old's ability to shave, the 45-year-old may
well have the edge with 30-odd years of shaving beneath
his belt. However, if we were to send the same 17-year-old
to barber school and train him intensively in the
foundations of good facial hair grooming he would (we
hope) return smarter, with the ability to shave more
efficiently and with a better understanding of what he was
trying to achieve.

For handstands at least, constant unexamined repetition of
an action is not the fastest way to improve. Instead it is the
paring down this action into its fundamental parts (see our
pillars — flexibility, specific strength, alignment etc. p6)
and the learning of them, along with the 'hows' *and* the
'whys'. It is a dedicated practice, but it's also an intelligent
one.

Before he signed off, I asked Reuben if he had to choose
one thing, one thing to offer as the golden ticket, the key to
handstand mastery — what would it be? He shrugged, as
if it was the most obvious thing in the world, "Learning
correct technique from the best coaches preferably in small
classes."

I thought of the traditional yoga set-up, of one on one
tuition or Pattabhi Jois's Mysore style of student to teacher
feedback, where all of the challenges that come with the
human package are catered for and celebrated.

We know there are handstand superheroes; super-humans walking amongst us or practising alongside us on the neighbouring mat, just waiting to pop upside down at a moment's notice or at the briefest of bat signals. But they couldn't always fly, they all had to start somewhere; underneath the cape and mask we're all human, some have just got better equipment and a Batmobile.

The CrossFit Gym Owner
Name: Larry
Age: 40s

Uber cool and unnervingly attractive, Larry owns a CrossFit gym and has the muscles to prove it. He has a fascinating brain and is exceptionally driven. Whatever he does, he dedicates energy to it and does it well. For somebody so talented he is also remarkably free from ego.

While it can be a driving force, ego can sometimes be a barrier to athletic progress. The hardest person to teach is the person who believes they don't need to learn anything. One of the greatest things about learning a hard skill is that usually those who are the most dedicated have the least amount of ego, unfortunately on the flip side those who have the least amount of skill often have an inflated sense of self importance. There are so many times when I have thought 'please, go work on yourself — maybe go to yoga (good yoga) — and then come back'. Equally there have been some happy instances of students walking through the door with an ego and leaving without one.

Larry understands what makes a skill. He works with himself the same way that he works with his CrossFit clients, he doesn't give them bigger weights if they are not ready for it and he doesn't let himself move onto the 'next big move' until he is sure he is ready for it.

Larry is a family man, he balances an intense job as a fireman as well as running a successful business. He is the guy who if you give some exercises to will actually do them, if a physio gives him exercises he will do them — not just complain that the physio couldn't fix him.

Handstands are great for folks like Larry — they are quantifiable, you can spot marked progress and Larry feeds off this. Unlike Sudhira, he doesn't need me around to make sure he'll do his training, he needs a personal training programme and then he needs the time to complete it.

The training plans in this book are for people like Larry — they are precise, they are laid out there for you and they will help you work towards an objective. Given the tools, Larry will dig the hole and plant the flower. I would stress that Larry is unusual, many of us need a toe-tapping supervisor or training buddy to prod, encourage and check our form while we dig.

Larry's Handstand Pillars

Specific Strength: 2/5
Endurance: 4/5
Alignment: 3/5
Consistency: 3/5
Balance: 2/5
Mobility/Flexibility: 2/5
Shape: 1/5

Larry's Handstand Exercises

Specific strength: Sainaa 4
Alignment: Blueberry Abs/3 Positions Against Wall
Consistency: Level up Consistency Exercise with 10 opportunities to hold each repetition for 10 secs
Balance: Balance Exercise x3
Shape: Basic Shape Set
Mobility/Flexibility: Hold a strap in between hands in front and then take over the head
Mobility/Flexibility: Straddle/active box split with a resistance band

Mobility/Flexibility: Take hands shoulder width apart on a bar or windowsill. Open as much as possible allowing chest to the floor without moving shoulders, tighten the abs and pull the ribs in (repeat x3 x10 secs each).

You are enough

– Jambo Truong

5. The (tangled) Web

I was not a sporty child. Even now the mention of organised sport conjures up images not of sun-spotted post-BBQ kick-arounds but of jogging sullenly around a damp running track in my school sports kit or the vicious Hunger Games-style arena that was Wednesday afternoon inter-house netball matches.

I did love books though. And it was this love of book learning that allowed me to cerebrally jostle my way to the front of the UCAS-crowd, to land a place at university.

I remember the acceptance letter arriving in the post and it might as well have been from Hogwarts. I hugged it to my chest, months of expectation melting away and I just knew everything would be ok.

Then October 2005 rolled around and with it the academic whirlwind of ambition, library dust and spinning deadlines swooshing by that determine the life of any overwhelmed undergraduate.

Something had to be done. Knowing that university is a time for casual experimentation and needing some serious distraction from those books that I had once clung to so dearly, I decided to dabble in the unthinkable.

Under the watchful eye of my hall-mate Athena, I bought my first pair of non-charity-shop trainers in about a decade and started turning up to sporting events.

Suddenly I was on the college football team, I rowed three times a week and had become a snack-bearing regular at Ultimate Frisbee tournaments. I had tried to dabble and had instead dived straight into the deep-end, sparkly new trainers first.

My once shiny trainers had got pretty muddy by the time I found Sarah's yoga class. Back in the Dark Ages where things were advertised in paper-format rather than solely on Facebook, I'd seen a poster pinned to a board in the Junior Common Room. It was a simple photocopied sheet informing us of time, location and price. The yoga didn't have a catchy or dynamic name, it was, simply, 'yoga'. You were invited simply to come and try it out, free for your first class.

"What do we wear?" I asked over the phone.

"Oh, just wear your pyjamas. It's not like we're doing exercise."

From then on dreams of boating trophies and soccerly success sloughed away and twice a week, blinking and bleary-eyed, I would find my way to the Trinity College Anson rooms. The room was beautiful in the way that all Oxford college rooms are beautiful; shiny wooden parquet floor, a few portraits of austere academic elders and a dreamy view of the spires peaking through the large neatly-framed windows, a subtle and consistent reminder of both the beauty present in the world and equally of our own relative insignificance within it. It was very yoga.

The majority of the other students there were senior citizens and would treat me a little like a visiting grandchild; checking that I was eating well (I was not eating well), was enjoying my studies (I was enjoying my studies), that I was doing my homework (I was not doing my homework). I would roll around slowly on a borrowed mat in what would indeed best be described as pyjamas, and gently my problems would melt from my muscles and slide off my bones. I would float back to my paper-strewn dorm room on a fluffy, meditative, yoga-stoned cloud.

I had tried to bust the stress by exhausting myself, but in yoga I had found a more time-efficient stress management system. This was a space to be safe, to be centered, and in an environment that constantly drove you to be the best, it was a rare hour free of competition and the desire to achieve.

In those first few years of rolling around on my mat I did not think in my wildest meditation-induced dreams that I would become a yoga teacher. Even if I'd known it was a viable option, that was absolutely *not* my career plan. No, I was going to go down a much more sensible route — I was going to be a professor, or an archaeologist or maybe some kind of Indiana Jones-inspired professor/archaeologist/ explorer super-combo. Yoga teaching had yet to accrue the Stateside-inspired shininess that the industry has today; studios were basic, the salaries small and the 'rockstar yogi' had not yet been invented. Upon questioning, the teacher Sarah likened her choice of profession to that of Morris-dancing: fun and full of joy but not exactly a sexy career move.

Whenever I look up 'what is yoga?' in my internal Encyclopedia I see a picture of Sarah. Glowing with the kind of health you only usually see on someone who owns their own allotment, Sarah has a willowy frame and eyes that shoot wisdom at you like laser beams. She balances her dual passions as a part-time yoga teacher and part-time antiquarian book dealer.

Four years into my pyjama-wearing, mat-rolling yoga phase I stopped being a university student and became a mural painter/waitress (super-combo). Money was tight. I had moved out of student accommodation and was now living in my friend's front room, sharing it with her collection of elegant 1940s film star biographies and even more elegant grandfather clocks. My diet had regressed to a heady mix of cafe food, red wine and caffeine. My yoga grandparents were, needless to say, appalled.

All of this essentially meant I was only able to afford the occasional class. On spotting my sporadic attendance, Sarah reacted in the way that she responds to most things — simply, efficiently and politely. In this instance, she simply refused to let me pay. As some kind of small tribute I would help tidy the props and pack them into (every yoga teacher's favourite tool) the Ikea bags at the end of each session.

I remember watching her, on one of the few occasions when she demonstrated anything, float gracefully into a headstand. "You don't even need any weight on the head," she insisted smiling and, to prove her point, hovering her head off the mat "See?"

Something in me wavered; this was another aspect of yoga I hadn't come across yet — this fancy headstand business. My yoga so far had been deliciously grounding and as such had been practised very reassuringly *close* to the ground. Sarah's feet on the other hand were sky high, her body completely inverted and yet she looked freakishly calm — happy even.

While collecting up the mats after the practice, I admitted sheepishly to Sarah about my worries regarding this strange new pose. Was I limited in my practice because I couldn't do this very cool, very awesome and what I still consider to be this very advanced pose? Sarah smiled, a smile that one might equally have used when watching someone try to 'pull' a door open clearly marked 'push'. A smile that meant that while I was trying, I hadn't yet quite grasped the concept.

"What if you didn't have an arm Ash? Or legs? Could you still master yoga?"

Sarah was right, I had heard the lesson that yoga wasn't all about the posture but I hadn't really taken it to heart. Seeing her switch her physical orientation so calmly had however flicked a switch in me; it had burned in me a desire to find a way to do the same.

I once heard yoga teacher Kathryn Budig say in a workshop that physical goals are important, not because of the shapes that you cut on your yoga mat but because these goals help prove to yourself that you can achieve something that you once thought was impossible. And I did think headstands were impossible, but I practised. A lot. I practised on my lunch breaks, walking my feet steadily inch by inch towards my nose in the cafe gardens, after work in the park, while waiting for buses or boiling the kettle, one particularly ill-advised attempt involving one of the grandfather clocks …and one day, after months (many many months) my toes did 'magically' start to hover off the ground.

Skip forward a little more than a decade and what was once the uncontested king of postures seems to have been replaced as the benchmark of 'strong practice' by its more technically advanced counterpart, the relatively new posture on the block, the handstand. Whatever the physical shape, the metaphor remains: that however challenging something appears, with enough effort the struggle can dissolve; that things, and the perception of those things, evolve.

Yoga is an ancient thing; a full body of wisdom that has shifted, ebbed and flowed for millennia. Right now the

trend seems to be the upside down but you never know,
maybe in ten years time we'll have ditched the Lycra and
instead have yogis rolling floppily around in their PJs on
the cover of the yoga magazines. Not today though —
today, stretch sells.

Every year the *Om Yoga and Lifestyle* magazine hosts a
number of *Om Yoga* shows, huge and exhilarating expos
dotted around the country where both yoga professionals
and enthusiastic students of all shapes, sizes and schools of
thought gather to mingle, stretch and peruse the collected
offerings. At any given conference you can spot the Rocket
yogis rubbing shoulders with the Jivamuktis, the Yogalates
crew buddying up with the Budokonites… It's basically
yoga heaven. But busier.

The first time I managed to get to one was in October, last
year. I'd been invited to help out my friend Dan on his stall
for his celebrated 'Yoga Like Water' teacher training
programme and, although prepped, was not in any way
prepared for what awaited me.

Gabby had agreed to drive and Will was curious, so all
three of us piled into Gabby's Nissan Micra on a wet and
blustery Saturday and headed to London. Four hours of
less-than-zen traffic jam later we arrived at Alexandra
Palace, damp, cramped and not feeling particularly yogic.
We were definitely in the minority.

We walked through the doors to an Aladdin's cave of
activity and yoga goodies: new-found-friend requests

zipped excitedly through the ether, bouncing around the stalls piled high with all kinds of yogic delights (whether by inspired plan or lucky coincidence, the frenetic buzz of mobile phones used to network and snap pictures was being helpfully and energetically balanced by the mountains of quartz crystal on display). The atmosphere was also bonkers with yoga classes, demonstrations, a market to buy your malas and an area to eat raw chocolate and/or meditate in case it all got too much to handle.

It was most definitely too much for me to handle. I wound my way single-mindedly through the stalls, in hindsight rudely dismissing kind offers of aura readings and chakra balancing. I tried to keep hold of Will, a tether in the maze, but inevitably lost him and Gabby to a blingy-looking stall selling 'gangster' yoga gear.

"Hey Ash, you made it!"

Dan Peppiatt, a dub-loving dreadlocked haven of yogic calm, all bandana and beaming smiles, rescued me from the tide and pulled me in for a hug. I dropped my things in a squishy pile, feeling lighter already.

"There are many unexplainable mysteries in life," Dan writes in his *Yoga Like Water* Spring newsletter, "but the skill of balancing on your hands should not be one of them." A former medical student with a penchant for surf and skateboards, Dan has a refreshingly pragmatic attitude towards yoga asana, finding as much spirituality in a gently

165

coasting wave as he does in a well-crafted *trikonasana* or downward-facing dog, or indeed a handstand.

Like most deep and meaningfuls, Dan and I had our 'so what's with all the handstands' chat in the snack aisle of Barnstaple Marks and Spencer's. Dan was currently prepping for a trip to India and was stocking up on tandoori flavoured crisps to inspire his kids to the wondrous flavours of the East.

"Weirdly people are more likely to listen when you ask them to sit still if they've seen you do something physically challenging."

The search had now moved onto an appropriately zesty dipping sauce.

"People are so desperate to be a 'master yogi' and they think that this handstand business is some sort of defining posture — a bit like a headstand used to be twenty years ago. I don't really know, I've probably taught hundreds or thousands of people in handstand workshops. Ninety percent of them will never actually manage an unsupported handstand simply because they don't have the necessary dedication. People want you to show them a simple trick that will save them from doing the hours and hours of work needed. Sadly, it doesn't exist."

I thought of Will and his weekly handstand training sessions, the time in the gym spent working the appropriate muscle groups, that unfathomable drive and dedication that he had to get upside down. If I was a yoga teacher shouldn't I be able to do this already? Wouldn't my hours on the mat just translate into a more easeful handstand practice? Just lift myself up pencil straight with zen and a good loud *Om*? Turns out not.

Dan recently told *Om Yoga* magazine that 'movement is movement; somebody made up every asana, they weren't suddenly delivered to us from above. I'm just continuing that organic process without the imaginary boundaries of there being a 'right' or a 'wrong' way to practise."[1] Just as the popularity of handstands has changed in the yoga scene as a whole, for Dan the role of handstands in his yoga has evolved equally organically over the years — from a dynamic peak to a more restorative element to be woven effortlessly into his time on (and as likely, off) the mat. For him the time of discipline and struggle has passed, now they are "totally effortless, I feel I could just hang in there forever."

"Well now you're here, I guess I can go and get my massage," an affirming squeeze on my slightly shell-shocked shoulder and he was off — navigating his way deftly towards a tent offering Thai Massages. Huh, so that was how he was keeping so chill.

As soon as his massage was over, Dan and his well-coiffed locks (his wife Gemma insists that he spends hours sculpting his dreads. Dan denies this) returned freshly stretched and shooed me off to investigate the rest of the

---

[1] Yoga Like Water. (Jan 2017). *Om Yoga and Lifestyle Magazine*, p. 52

show's offerings. Gabby and Will had also turned up, so together we wove our way to the photo booth.

Om Yoga had set up an area where a professional photographer would snap your picture which then the great and powerful Oms would review and perhaps if you were lucky, choose it for their next front cover. A line of hopeful yogis awaited, all hoping to make it onto the coveted cover spot. We joined the queue hesitantly.

"What shall we do?" I whispered frantically.

Gabby started limbering up her wrists. "How about me in a handstand, you in a split with your foot on your head?" I gulped and started jogging on the spot.

Thankfully we were there for a good 20 minutes awaiting our turn (Will had wandered off to hunt out the elusive men's yoga offerings — amidst a sea of neon Lycra print, unsurprisingly, there were very few); yogini after yogini taking their turn in front of the lights, camera and… really, *eka pada rajakapotasana* (king pigeon) — again?

Gabby had moved from her wrist exercises to gliding deftly through some handstand shapes. As so often happens when Gabby goes upside down in a yoga setting, a small open-mouthed mob had begun to form.

"How are you so controlled?" One girl who had just attempted to headstand for the camera asks, clearly awestruck but anxious to know the secret of Gabby's enviable ease upside down. "Where did you learn how to do this? Your handstands are about the best I've ever seen!"

Another said simply, "Wowza."

"She's a handstand teacher," I say pointlessly, feeling a protectiveness towards my friend and also a need to let everyone know 'this isn't just yoga'. I add, "Circus" as if that explains everything.

When finally we reach the front of the queue, the photographer, tired from a long day, looked slightly jaded with the idea of another yogi putting their foot over, on top of, or around their face. I couldn't blame him. Almost sheepishly, I stretch out into my extended split *hanumanasana* and tickle my nose with my toes. Gabby gracefully floats her feet skywards, a natural in front of the camera she moves her legs and body position artfully with the photographer's instructions. I stay stoic, and just a little wobbly.

Snap snap snappety snap.

Sarah had told me it wasn't about the pose. She was right of course but as I started to breathe strong wave-like inhales to drown out the clickety clack of the camera lens, right now, I thought, it *is* about the photo. So grin, flex, and just keep breathing.

A few months after the *Om Yoga* show I see the magazine's cover girl smiling serenely from the Health and Lifestyle section of WHSmiths. The pose isn't particularly difficult, instead she is in a heels up goddess pose, arms crossed artistically in front creating a captivating zigzag of pink and electric blue angles. She is the perfect yoga poster girl — strong, healthful and full of hope.

Not a handstand in sight.

'With My Witches.' I was reading the slogan on Jambo 'The Dragon' Truong's jumper through half-closed eyelids. I was seated as part of a circle watching as he smudged Dan's studio, wafting his sage stick around like a smoking magic wand, inviting any unwelcome spirits to kindly please fuck off out of his yoga ceremony.

It was a few weeks later and we were in Devon on one of Dan's Yoga Like Water teacher training weekends.

Jambo's Welsh inflected laugh filled the room as easily as the smoke; he grabbed his drum, squidged out the butt of the sage and rearranged his stripy fisherman's pants so he could sit. Our eyes and ears opened, expectant.

"There were two monks," Jambo began, enveloping us all immediately in his hypnotic tones and in his story, "who loved to sing. One was a fantastic singer, and the other — well, not so much. They would sing every morning but soon, feeling a little shy, the less able singer stopped singing." He pauses, just to check the room is breathing. I up my *ujjayi* obediently by about 15%.

"Hearing only the more operatic monk's morning songs, an angel appeared before the first monk who had stopped singing. 'Why have you stopped singing?' the angel asked. 'Why would anyone want to listen to me,' said the monk, 'when you could listen to him?'"

bo exhales, echoing the angel's frustration and ruffling gon wings. "'Do you think we care? Do you think we have, I don't know, Monks Got Talent up here in heaven?! No! Sing because it brings you *joy*!'"

Because it brings you joy.

Jambo's gaze sprawled over the room, a dragon on the prowl for the golden gifts of those in the circle. How many of us had decided not to try something because we'd decided we weren't 'good' or 'perfect' enough, because we knew there was someone who could do it 'better'? How beautiful would it be if the only question we asked was, would it bring me joy? Would it delight my spirit? It would? Well then let's go!

That day Jambo was teaching us, quite literally, how to march to the beat of our own drum. He had brought his own drum with him and he struck it as he sang. "The power is within you," he pointed his baton at each of us, punctuating his point. "Let Great Spirit come. Hey!"

It took four more spirit songs before we were all limber/tired enough for the subject of social media to rear its many Insta-Twitter-Google-faces.

"How as teachers can we maintain integrity whilst still making a living?" Samantha, already a teacher, asked fidgeting with her loose and logo-less yoga tee. "I mean, how do we choose what to post online?"

Another quieter voice piped up from across the circle. "People don't really want to see us in meditative poses, just the more 'exciting' ones. Why do you reckon that we've got so obsessed with them? All these handstands and stuff?"

Jambo twirled his drum baton. He breathed loudly as he thought, I on the other hand held my breath in a very unyogi-like way. *This* was it. *This* was my answer.

"You need to sell yoga. And asana is sexy" (inhale) "you can clothe it, you can market it, you can buy a mat for it." (Inhale) "The most you're going to buy for meditation is a cushion."

Jambo smiled, a very toothy dragon smile and the scales fell from my blissed-out yoga brain. Was it really that simple?

Handstands are popular because of… sex?

I understood handstands were sexy of course, I mean who hasn't been in a yoga class, seen a guy floating into a handstand out of the corner of your eye, noticed the studio lighting get a bit fuzzy and suddenly, a trick of the light, the handstander is magically transformed into Ryan Gosling sitting in a bar deftly playing the piano in *La La Land*?

For me it is the dedication, discipline and competence to master a skill that is at the root of the attraction (of handstands, not of Ryan Gosling) but throw in the muscular physicality usually associated with the pose and yes, of *course* they were a particular kind of sexy.

And with that brand of sexiness, as Jambo pointed out, comes a whole raft of marketing possibilities — marketing possibilities that the social media machine has taken full advantage of.

Social media, particularly the realms of Facebook and Instagram where the yogis like to hang out (mostly upside down), is broadly a visual marketplace and asana, as the visual arm of the yoga body, has made itself very much at home there — so much so that other aspects of the yoga system (mantra, mudra, pranayama and meditation amongst others) find it difficult to find a place.

When scrolling through a newsfeed or flicking through a magazine, these tricky poses have the wonderful double pause effect of "Hmm, I wonder how they did that?" and "Hey, could *I* do that?" The sex, and the stretch, sells. And while a slim, muscular model rocking out a one-armed hand balance whilst wearing stretchy shiny leggings may not be everyone's aspirational cup of tea, we are finally (albeit in a slightly askance manner) finally being asked to admire a body for what it can *do* rather than just how it looks.

The Clothing Conversation

People are always watching… and when they watch and they see this strong human being living in their body, imperfections and all, someone will go 'I can do that too. I can let go of my pain and I can feel strong.'

— Kathryn Budig

Much like my other tiny feminist heroines (Gabby, Buffy the Vampire Slayer) you have the sense that the beautiful blonde Kathryn Budig wakes up with cute woodland animals plaiting her hair, yawns, cooks up a hearty breakfast and then decides how she should kick some evil butt that day.

Budig's evil-butt-kicking days (in between international and online teaching, writing, podcasting and cooking up delicious recipes) are mostly spent battling online body shaming.

A recent Instagram campaign invited her 200,000 followers to post a photograph of themselves that they had previously hidden or hated, next it was to place an affirming post-it note on an area of the body that they were the most insecure about and share it. An empowering message in a world (the yoga world not excluded) obsessed with the lithe and limber silhouette.

I remember seeing Budig's collaboration with Jasper Johan for his 'Body as Temple' campaign for ToeSocks in *Yoga Journal*. A true athlete, her naked (she was wearing socks) monochrome form looked healthy and strong, tensed in an impressive arm balance — her focus fixed. At seeing the artful nudes sporting the pages of *Yoga Journal*, a number of yoga's most prestigious elders wrote in to the magazine to express their shock and disappointment. Budig took this in her stride; the campaign was getting attention and as a result so was her charity 'Poses for Paws' that raises money for animal shelters. It had worked.

Feeling good and becoming confident in my own skin are the primary gifts that yoga has given me and many other people I know and now teach. A part of that confidence for me is knowing that you can wear (or in Kathryn's case, not wear) anything you like — whether that's finding comfort in a boyfriend's old t-shirt or splashing out on a new pair of yoga shorts.

Brands like Sweaty Betty, Hard Tail, Lululemon and Under Armour exist because the market is there, men and women don't want to dress differently when they are doing exercise than they would do when they aren't. I have a friend Tara who is possibly the most beautiful human you are ever likely to meet in real life. She is not someone who needs to exercise to feel well, or who particularly enjoys it. However upon moving to Bristol and seeing the waves of runners pounding their way under Clifton suspension bridge and across the Downs she decided that it was something she'd like to try.

The evening of her first run was a little chilly so without thinking about it she swept a favourite pashmina around her shoulders and left the house at a brisk trot, cashmere billowing behind her in the crisp Clifton air. While Tara could turn anything into a trend without even trying, the pashmina turned out not to be the most useful of running accessories. Her taste however did not conceive of her leaving the house looking anything less than fabulous, not because she was proud but that was how she felt most comfortable. The friendly staff at Sweaty Betty showed her a selection of chic fashionable pieces that could keep her feeling herself when she was exercising, and her dilemma was solved.

I add this example because there is a trend to rage against the non 'traditional' in yoga or in anything that we love, as if adding something new will take away from the old that we hold so dear. Whether it's a cool new clothing brand, an 'out there' fusion style, a crazy arm balance workshop or even the playing of Rihanna in class, as consciousness grows it is good to remember that every way of looking at yoga will help include a person that would have otherwise not looked twice had it not been for that new perspective.

As well as finding a new opportunity to stretch your wardrobe (and bank balance), starting any new exercise brings with it an increased awareness of our bodies; a relationship forms between our minds and this machine that carries us around — for many of us for the first time. Yoga in particular focuses on this communion between brain (mind/soul/spirit) and body, bringing with its practice the unique gift of acceptance of our physical form rather than an emphasis on improvement or change. We are asked to love ourselves, with all of our perfections and all of our flaws (whatever our wardrobe).

No doubt there is a wave of bringing the sexy back into yoga, whether that is by fancy poses on posters, palatially zen studios, luxury outfits or wiggling your newly painted toenails in a forward fold. And it might be that we are trying to whitewash what is at its heart a gritty practice of peeling back the layers of ourselves, and this of course is all gateway stuff to a deeper understanding of yoga as a whole… but, and this is just me, I do find it easier to clear my mind when I know that my boobs aren't going to fall out of my top.

I still do my yoga in my pyjamas in the morning. I do not need to be sold special yoga pyjamas (although I bet they exist). I have also tried handstanding in my pyjamas, and let me tell you — that shit does *not* work. If someone is asking me to put my foot behind my head, do a 2 hour sweaty yoga-thon or go upside down I 'need' (ha! Ok, 'prefer') the stretchy pants and the techno fabric and most especially the near industrial scaffolding that a well-designed sports bra offers.

All of the fabulous props that the wider yoga industry offers us now (whether it is a new kind of yoga block, a special grippy mat or peacock-printed yoga pants) are designed to help us ease into our yoga practice, make it easier, make it more joyful. Maybe one day we won't need them, but for now I am so happy that they exist and in so many many pretty colours.

The most important things in my life are God, my family, and my Instagram account. And not necessarily in that order.

— JP, Ultra Spiritual

Every year Gabby and Richard organise the Bristol Acro Intensive. It is two full days of crazed circus monkeying about — people clambering on each other, chalky high-fives, hurried calorie consumption and watching our friend Jonny backward somersault at any given opportunity. Will teaches the Acroyoga, I lead the well-earned end of the day massage and Gabby teaches the handstanding component.

At the end of every weekend the teaching staff retreat *en masse* to the pub — the pub chosen for its proximity, excellent selection of local ales, picturesque rural frontage and the checkerboard of picnic tables in the beer garden — the perfect setting of course for an 'impromptu' group handstand photo.

I personally don't truly understand social media. I was (strongly) encouraged by my peers to get a Facebook account at university when it turned out everything was organised on there and by default I was missing out on all of the best parties. It lay (to my friend's frustration) dormant for a few years before I left to work abroad and then it sprang back into my life as the perfect means to assure those same friends that yes I was still alive and hey, look at all the coconuts I'm drinking.

We all have our own reasons for using the social media platforms: as communication; as advertising; as a handy distraction when pretending not to listen to that awkward conversation on the train and not forgetting the worthwhile pursuit of collating and sharing endlessly hilarious cat videos. For some it is a way to check in, for others a way to check out and for some of us it is a place to post photos of our friends handstanding on beer garden benches.

Eventually we moved the party inside and the barman came over to clear away some of our empties.

"I saw you guys doing those handstands, very impressive," his voice carrying over the chinking of glass and the barrage of circus chat. Those in the group who had handstood on his tables smiled appreciatively in the way professionals do, as if he were talking to a group of accountants congratulating them on well filled-out tax returns.

The barman continued, "Yeah, my friend can handstand. He handstands all the time. You should see his Instagram account — he's in Lanzarote, handstanding on a beach; now he's by a waterfall, handstanding; in the Cotswolds, handstands there too; Tesco's car park… I mean, we get it Derek. You can do a handstand."

We all looked guiltily into our pints laughing short sharp awkward laughs. After a long pause Richard replied, "Um, you might not want to follow any of us on Instagram then."

The Lawyer
Name: Georgina
Age: 30s

Every time I meet Georgina I am amazed; beautiful, confident, glowing with health I met her when she strolled into my workshop rosy-cheeked and smiling, as if she'd walked out of a Sweaty Betty catalogue (I mean obviously she was not actually sweating).

Georgina is a remarkably capable student, considering she has zero background in any performance discipline. She is an ex-runner, a former Ashtangi and a ballet dabbler. Georgina sought me out as she was searching for something physically beautiful and challenging for her body to learn. She was always in awe of the shiny acrobatic Instagram posts of beach inversions, long tanned legs and cartwheels in the sunset. She always tells me that I have such an exciting life but, the grass always being greener, I would love to be Georgina. She is wonderfully sorted; a fantastic mum, a strong professional and has the ability to look immaculately put together even at a moment's notice (now THAT is a super power). When I arrived at George's house for our first private I saw that she had a picture of a girl doing a straight one-arm on her fridge, out of place in her immaculately designed house. It took half a year for me to tell her that that handstand was a cheeky snapshot caught mid-fall rather than a reflection of actual skill and like much of what we see online unrealistic, and ultimately, unreal.

There is a lot of inspiration out there, but there is also a lot of negativity. Georgina put some pictures of her dancing online and the reaction she got was very upsetting, people scrutinising her form and giving her unasked for and needlessly harsh criticism.

Georgina already has a tendency towards comparison, always believing that she should be better and also that she is worse than she is. Her progress has been remarkable, but we have had to talk about her putting too much pressure on herself.

She has since taken herself off social media and instead of posting the pictures online, instead she sends them to friends or to me — pictures of her cartwheeling joyously in her back garden, not worrying whether someone else could get their legs straighter. The practice has become hers again and she now talks much more about how it feels rather than how it looks. After our training sessions I will leave and I know she will get straight back on her training for another hour at least — because she's capable and dedicated, but also because she absolutely loves it!

Georgina's Handstand Pillars

Specific Strength: 3/5
Endurance: 3/5
Alignment: 3/5
Consistency: 3/5
Balance: 3/5
Mobility/Flexibility: 3/5
Shape: 3/5

Georgina's Handstand Exercises

Specific strength: Sainaa 4 / Plank to pike x3
Endurance: 3x30 secs shape focus
Alignment: 3 Positions Against Wall / Pike reps
Consistency: Consistency exercise with hand and head variations plus balance set at the end/Pushing/Pulling exercise for highlighting failure areas
Balance: Balance Exercise x3
Shape: Basic Shape Set (x5 secs) Variation of entrances into handstand / Cartwheel/Tuck, straddle, pike sets / Sliding tucks down the wall / Press preps / Scorpion / Forearm stand
Mobility/Flexibility: Box split with resistance band / Active leg reps / L+R split training / Hip flexor isolated stretches / Massage ball work for ITB

"Do. Or do not. There is no try."

— Yoda, The Empire Strikes Back

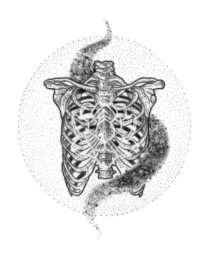

6. Yin, Yang and Yanger

The day Gabby was told she wasn't going to walk again, she went down to the gym and did handstands.

That was the day she met Matt.

You can rarely spot the handstanders. The secret to their fiendish disguise is that you weirdly don't have to be pretty, tanned or dressed in beachwear to be good at them which annoyingly makes these handstanders a lot harder to spot in real life than on Instagram.[2]

A CrossFitter's toned midriff and protein shake you can spot a good gym-floor distance off, a yogi by their tattoo, shiny string of mala beads or twinkling Om around their neck but handstanders no, handstanders are The Power Rangers, the undercover athletes, of the sporting world. They belong to a secret club of those who are willing to practise.

If you had to pick one out of a crowd though, you'd pick Matt Pasquet. An unassuming yet muscular presence with the broadest shoulders not to be found on the Welsh rugby team. At the time he met Gabby, Matt was still a handstand hobbyist — a builder by trade. The day when Gabby hobbled into the gym he was there training breakdance moves with his friends. By complete accident, Gabby had happened upon the HQ of this secret handstand practice club and quickly found herself accepted, soon to be swept up on Matt's broad shoulders and into his arms. She began training with them.

---

[2] By the way, if you look at Matt Pasquet's Instagram account (@mattpasquet) which I did in preparation for our interview, you will as likely see a picture of a Borneon moth, an African python (#greenasfuck) or 'that time me and @dan_handstand had a pet skink for an entire afternoon #goodtimes' as anything remotely acrobatic. Really interesting if, for this book anyway, entirely irrelevant.

She became such a regular participant that Nat (one of Matt's friends and recent stuntman in Christian Bale's *Batman*) had had just about enough of the escalating sexual tension and demanded that Gabby give Matt her "digits".

"He wants my digits? He can ask me himself," she had replied shortly.

So he did.

The year they began dating, Gabby was essentially having full reconstructive surgery on her leg. Not an easy time to foster a budding romance, but Matt was a welcome and supportive source of stillness in a stormy and uncertain time. When Gabby finally got into Rosny, (being the Goldilocks combo of discipline, determination and dimensions that they required to fill the missing flyer's shoes) Matt went too. That is, from having no previous acrobatic experience he auditioned for two circus schools and got into both — Rosny (ENACR) and DOCH in Stockholm. After a year together at circus school the pair parted on friendly terms with Gabby returning to the UK and Matt heading onto further training in Sweden.

The possession of anything begins in the mind.

— Bruce Lee

Half a decade later and we are standing on the porch of Matt's parents' place in Cheltenham. "There are some strangers at the door," Matt's mum Ellie calls into the house, pulling Gabby in for tight one-armed hug.

Her face is still beaming (the smile of a mother whose famous son has just popped in between international tour dates) as we are ushered unceremoniously into the house; Gabby (clearly a regular in the Pasquet household) leads the way. I notice a newly framed picture placed carefully on the kitchen table, ready to be put up, pride of place, above the mantlepiece. It is a photograph of a spotlighted Matt, all muscle and intense expression, balancing on one arm in front of a dramatic dip-dyed sunset. Even the pros, it seems, can't resist a good sunset.

Having spoken to Reuben about the years of rigour and monotonous man-hours that go into creating a near-perfect handstand, those who I see performing this skill have started exuding an almost sage-like quality. Struggling through months, years of training for a shape that lasts just a few minutes or less, kind of like the monks who spend days making mandalas out of butter just to let them melt in the Tibetan sun or the artists who choose to make cathedrals from sand just to let them be washed away in the next inevitable tide. The handstands, art and sand sculptures may fade, but the skill and the mind that created them remains intact.

Matt had this same meditative air around him, and when I mentioned what I thought to be an incredibly deep and astute observation to Gabby (sands of time, transience etc.) she replied quickly with "Oh yep, absolutely. Makes perfect sense. You know Matt's a 5th degree blackbelt in Kung Fu too? Very zen."

Professional handbalancer and martial artist. No wonder
Matt Pasquet seemed so chill, I thought. He is basically
Yoda, or the old turtle from Kung Fu Panda. I bet he
meditates too.

Kung Fu is a famously long game. Despite what Jackie
Chan and Jaden Smith would have us believe, you can not
movie-montage your way to mastery in a few short months
— to come close to anything near a complete
understanding of the discipline takes a decade or more. To
get that good and to practise for that long you need a
certain mindset; Matt has that mindset.

We are sitting at the kitchen table, hot coffee cradled in
our hands. I want to know how Kung Fu training has
influenced Matt's handbalancing career. Liquid sloshes out
of Gabby's polkadot mug as she eagerly leaps in with the
'fact' that while she can handstand she could 'never be a
handbalancer'.

Gabby's handstand teacher Sainaa's favourite phrase for
her is "Gabby, you could be good but you laaaazy." This,
according to Gabby, is one hundred percent true. "I get
distracted way too easily" she explains.

Matt shakes his sandy-haired head, in a way that makes it
seem that he is both agreeing and disagreeing at the same
time. "Everyone has the same potential body-wise." I stare
down into my coffee letting the wisdom sink in, everyone
has the same potential. He knocks his index finger to his
brain, "but it is this that makes the difference."

Gabby starts to giggle, "It's just the dedication, I could
never do it! I mean, it would be 6am and I'd look out the
window to see him making Kung Fu shapes in my

garden." She grins, looking at Matt, "he also has a particular need to have an even number of biscuits left in a packet. He even counts them, which is super weird." She picks a digestive out of the packet left open on the table and snaps it in half, punctuating her point and staring Matt straight in the face as she does it.

Trying to steer the conversation away from the digestives and biscuits in general, a topic on which I could have given both of them some serious wisdom on, I ask Matt whether it was the disciplined focus that was the biggest cross-over between his Kung Fu and his handstand training. Matt nods, pretending to not look at the now odd-numbered open packet.

"Oh also," he adds as an aside, making it clear that this information is much less important, "I had the core development. I could always lift myself into a handstand, I just couldn't stay there. I mean I had the strength, I just didn't know how to use it."

Gabby and I share a glance. Yep, super weird.

Being so focused on one discipline Matt never wanted to be boxed into a corner or to be so fixed in one way of movement, he wanted to explore the whole world of martial arts and so started practising the softer flows of Tai Chi.

Tai Chi is rooted in Taoism, a philosophy that states that everything is composed of opposites — the soft and hard, the accepting and the striving, the yin and the yang, the inhale and the exhale. This 'internal' flow was developed as a complement to the 'external', powerful art of Kung Fu. It celebrates life's natural balance. Most serious Kung

187

Fu practitioners temper their stronger training with this fluid style. "They know," says Matt, "that if they are expelling energy in their more rigorous practice they need to replenish it elsewhere." They recognise a need for balance, not just training hard, depleting energy and then collapsing. I think of the numbers of hardcore acrobats that I see in my softer more breath-centric yoga classes, a contrasting internal practice to their more external training, and I send a little love their way.

Matt is teaching his mum breathing techniques he has learned through his martial arts training, specifically Qi Gong, another internal replenishing practice. The shining bubbly Ellie who opened the door to us is currently undergoing daily radiotherapy and chemo for lung cancer, a cancer which has claimed three quarters of her lung.

Matt lifts his hands in the air in a motion of surrender. "Look, I am not a hippy." I nod, I know lots of hippies Matt and you are not one of them. "And I know it sounds odd when you label something but I mean of course Qi exists — Qi is just energy." He leans in, sweeping his hands in wide arching decisive movements — pausing for a moment — his arms make shapes in the air as he continues.

"If you are trying to move your energy you are thinking positively — you are sending positive messages to a part of your body. You've seen the Shaolin monks using their heads to break planks of wood, even concrete? They are sending their attention but more they are sending their breath, to parts of their body so that they can take the hit by creating a buffer."

Hitting my head repeatedly against a plank of wood could be a fairly accurate description of my handstand journey thus far. My handstands themselves usually last for about a breath. More precisely, they last for about the time that I can hold my breath. I inhale as I prepare, as if I am a sniper aiming at perfect balance — if I dare to breathe I will clearly wobble, miss the target and instead shoot the bodyguard or some poor underpaid personal assistant.

Still holding my breath, I kick up and… "Oh my god, I'm in a handstand! I'm in handstand?! Really?" At this point I usually stop being in a handstand and start being more akin to one of those wavy inflatable tube men that you see outside service stations.

Apparently there is another way.

Watch how a baby breathes. Watch carefully enough and you will see the belly move, inhale the belly expands, exhale the belly flattens. Through ageing and all of the added responsibilities that accompany it, people's breath patterns change — often relying too heavily on the chest while the belly gets crunched underneath a desk or squished daily behind a steering wheel.

In handstands you are invited to get back to that baby breath and breathe low, minimising the movement of the ribs and therefore the break in the shape that breathing high in the chest can create. Gabby illustrates this by taking her shoulders to her ears and pushing upwards: "if I breathe into my ribs I will change my shape — if I breathe deep and low I won't, I will stay fixed."

To investigate the role of breath in handstands more fully, Gabby set up an appointment for us with personal trainer Toby Wells. The first time I met Toby he reminded me of a youthful university professor; enthusiastic and with an ebullient love of learning and the body. A university professor that is, with a strict weight-lifting regime or one who has perhaps recently been bitten by a radioactive spider (and as a consequence is a little embarrassed at all of the overt musculature popping out of his M&S cardigans).

My handstand session with Toby begins not in the air, not on my palms, but flat on my back on a massage table.

Gabby is peeking at me behind her iPhone, the camera of which is fixed steadfastly on my breathing that Toby is inspecting diligently.

We are doing a movement assessment for intra-abdominal pressure "So what you want to do is engage the anterior core, yes these muscles here." Yep, I nodded, I was feeling them, "and then use them to draw the ribs down."

At this point Toby did something really strange, he picked up my trainer and placed it on my belly. "I usually use a book," he shrugged, "now inhale through your nose and exhale through pursed lips. Breathe."

20 minutes ago we had been sipping strong coffees in the cafe next door and I'd been giving an impassioned, heartfelt speech about how yoga was "like, all about the breath." I'd even scribbled down Iyengar's *Light on*

Pranayama on a paper napkin and thrust it at Toby urging him to read it.

I was there that morning primarily as a willing mannequin: either Gabby or Toby would ask me to lift up an arm, internally or externally rotate it and then put it back down again. We have three planes of motion: the sagittal, the frontal and the transverse, which we weave in, around and between. If you are limited in one plane or area of your body then you are inclined to rob movement from another plane or area. This was what happening with me; I could not (still at the point of typing this, can not) move my arms fully over my head. As a consequence I was losing the connection across my anterior (front) core, flaring my chest and sticking my butt out like Daffy Duck.

Back on the massage table, I can not breathe. Despite Toby's gentle urging to engage my abdominals, my ribs flare disobediently and my shoulders edge towards my ears; my thoracic spine lifts making my chest puff up like a balloon.

"Ok, so let's try something different." I flop over onto my front, trying not to think about the lineage of ancient yogic breathers I was disappointing by my inability to command my body do what it was bloody well told.

We are now doing a breathing exercise to relax the muscles, one that would help anyone — acrobats and 'muggles' alike.

"Oops, sorry — vampire hands," Toby — imagine more simply a younger, taller, more bearded Hugh Grant — very Englishly apologises for the slightly chilly palms that he is using to encourage me to breathe laterally. It takes five or six guided rounds with his hands on my rib cage before my back lengthens and I return to a relaxed molten state on the table. Through my controlled exhales I can hear Gabby's trainers squeak as she bounces up and down, the phone jiggling in her hand.

"Isn't it amazing! It's like it's *all* about the breath!"

Toby is equally as gleeful, nodding enthusiastically at Gabby, like we are all co-conspirators in this handstand anatomical alchemy. Which I suppose we are.

"Yes, exactly! The breath! Dysfunctional breathing means limited intra-abdominal pressure which means limited core stability and no structure to your handstand!"

Uh huh. So basically, magic.

The Juggler
Name: Jon
Age: Mid 20s

Circus is a broad art form and as such I often get circus folk coming to me as students who are specialists in branches other than acrobatics. My student Jon for example is a juggler, wanting to add another string to his circus bow, he decided to learn to handstand; not wanting to ruin his wrists, he sought out some professional help in learning to handstand. He calls me 'G Dog' and I love it.

As a juggler, Jon has a highly tuned body-brain connection and is able to apply technique quickly. However a typical session of ours will sound like this: "This is the one, THIS is the one, no this one. This one? Come on Jon, Come on." It sounds like the self-encouragement would work. It doesn't. What it does is rev-up Jon's naturally nervous energy when what handstands need really is calm and a certain grounded energy. If you see handbalancers train, if you remember Reuben on p144, they are almost meditative in their stillness.

The result is that Jon gets exhausted quickly. You would think that a juggler would have the perfect approach to handstand training: drop the ball, pick it up, drop the ball, pick it up. It's all very zen. But it is because Jon is used to being so proficient in another skill that he sometimes expects too much of himself, thinking that he can translate this into nailing a handstand in four weeks. Like Ash who had the idea that with so many years of yoga behind her, she should be able to pop straight into a press handstand or I would be any good at yoga. These are different skills, requiring different muscles and developing different mindsets. I also remind Jon that as with juggling, this handstand business is going to take some time.

I tried the breathing technique that Toby used with Ash (p188) with Jon and after 5 breaths I started to see Jon's whole energy change.

And if you are like John, honestly, just breathe. 10 long deep breaths before you attempt your consistency training will work wonders. Apply patience, there is a fine line between being driven and being rushed.

When I teach those that already do a performance discipline whether that is juggling, pole or aerial — something that will potentially be put on stage — I train them in something called 'environmental difference'. It is important that performers be trained in staying within their technique despite what they are feeling, what is going on around them or how much adrenaline is coursing through their veins. You think handstanding is hard, try handstanding on a turning disco ball with lights flashing and someone smacking your bum saying "don't hurt yourself love." Oh the glamorous circus life.

Jon's Handstand Pillars

Specific Strength: 3/5
Endurance: 2/5
Alignment: 3/5
Consistency: 2/5
Balance: 1/5
Mobility/Flexibility: 2/5
Shape: 1/5

Jon's Handstand Exercises

Specific strength: Sainaa 4 / 7 minutes in heaven
Endurance: 3 x 30 secs endurance position against wall focusing on shape
Alignment: 3 Positions Against Wall / Pike reps / Plank to pike
Consistency: Consistency set x3, on 4th rep, holding for 20 secs
Balance: Balance Exercise x3
Shape: Basic Shape Set (5 secs per shape)
*Mobility/Flexibility: Hold a strap in between hands in front and then take over the head/Box split with a resistance **band***

"Don't think. FEEL. It's like a finger pointing at the moon. Do not concentrate on the finger, or you will miss all of the heavenly glory."

— Bruce Lee

7. The Magic

The first yoga teacher who taught me handstands as part of her class was Denise Payne. This 54-year-old Arizona-born firecracker has been studying yoga since she was 15; raised as a Sikh, for the first five years she studied mantra (chants) and mudra (movements of the hands) before finally being invited to approach asana when she was 20.

In class I would gaze studiously as she planted her strong arms, inked in multi-coloured chakra spirals, lotus flowers (and Ganesha) on the ground and gracefully lift up into balances I had only ever seen before in books.

The first year I studied with her, some way through a Power Yoga class after demo-ing a particularly intricate transition, a student called out "You make it look so easy!" Crackling with an electric intensity Denise scanned the room until she caught the man's eye, he was at the back of the room and like all of us was staring in utter fascination at the yoga powerhouse that was in front of him.

"What do you do?" The man paused.

Denise insisted, politely, "what's your job?"

"I'm an architect," he replied nervously, as if not quite sure whether it was the right answer.

"Well, I bet you make that look easy." She gestured to her yoga mat, "*this* is my job."

As well as a powerful physical practice, 30-plus years of yoga has also gifted Denise with the unnerving capacity to look at you and within you and call you on your crap. She has the grandmotherly quality that those teachers that have lived with yoga the longest embody — deeply compassionate, endlessly patient, but equally unafraid to kick your ass, knowing that this really is the only way you'll learn.

I remember one particular inversions class, focusing that morning on my then seemingly insurmountable challenge

196

pose of headstand. On being told that we were under no circumstances allowed to hurl ourselves into the posture, a number of the class grumbled in mutinous dissension.

Denise sighed, an exasperated exhale which indicated that this was not the first room of students to dislike the instruction to 'not hurt yourself'.

She spun on her heels, making sure her chastisement encompassed everyone. "Excuse me yogis if I give a *fuck* about your cervical spine." She gazed around the room, eyes fiery and alive, 'yes we wear the jewellery, buy the t-shirts, get the tattoos — but are we willing to do the practice?"

To help us in this practice she would give us handstand homework to bounce off the wall with our feet — not to rest there but to attack it, passionately kick up and down and then when we crumpled, exhausted, she would smile kindly and say "it's just a memory, and not even an accurate one," and then encourage us to get up and try again. Because it's only a wall, it's only yoga, it's only a handstand and you are bigger than it.

Denise teaches a strong Power Yoga class, gloriously punctuated with handstands and arm balances. Denise explains, "it's always been my philosophy to do the hard stuff on the mat so that it's like our training ground. We do the hard stuff here, we learn how to be joyful, we learn how to breathe calmly, so that we train ourselves to handle all that stress when we leave the mat."

In 2011 Denise began teaching yoga at Kerobokan Prison in Bali at the request of Myuran Sukamaran, one of the 'Bali Nine' convicted of drug trafficking in April 2005.

Denise still goes in and teaches these 20 or 30 prisoners
yoga every week. Not an easy, calming class, Denise says
but a proper 'work out'.

Myuran (Myu) immediately became a committed yoga
student; death row inmate and Power Yoga teacher formed
a fast and lasting friendship.

When Myu was interviewed a couple of months before his
death and asked whether he would sit or stand for his
execution, his reply was, "I just want to do a handstand."
As an impassioned response to Myu's looming death
sentence Denise launched her online mercy campaign with
hashtag 'handstands for Myu.' She posted a photograph of
herself everyday in a handstand on social media, hundreds
of others joined in using the same tags.

For Myu's last meal he ordered pizzas for himself and the
guards and while he was not allowed to be in a handstand,
he faced the firing squad without a blindfold.

Handstands turn our world upside down, but for those
whose worlds are already upside down? As Denise says we
can but hope that the grace and the strength that we
acquire on the mat, if we work at it, will carry through to
our life beyond the mat.

It is this, even more than all of the physically seductive
beauty that these challenging poses embody, that is
perhaps the best gift that these aspirational postures have
to offer.

I was once told that if you asked a dog to look at the moon
by pointing at it, it would only stare at your finger, not
seeing the abstract, the unreachable, the divine that was

beyond. I tried this with a friend's dog, an excitable terrier/spaniel cross called Molly. Her dark wet pools of eyes widened as I pointed up into the cosmos, the singular shining orb illuminating St Andrew's Park. "Look girl — moon." Her tail wagged expectantly. I shifted my hand slightly so I was now pointing to a different square of sky, void of anything but inky blackness. Molly's head shifted too. As clever as she was she had no concept of the heavenly glory that the moon offers to us humans, that even after we have stepped on it and even planted a flag on its face, we continue to look at it in wonder.

As I looked at Molly's excitement at following my, to my mind rather ordinary, finger as it zoomed across the night sky I wondered if we too were concentrating so acutely on the tangible, that we were missing some of the magic that lay beyond these postures.

Scrolling through my phone I am like Molly, attention flicking greedily from one thing to the next — a graceful press into handstand, a shiny leotard, an exciting new yoga craze, an acrobat balancing pencil straight in one-arm…

Look, moon.

It is magic, this ability to stand on your hands. A magic that is created not with a pinch of fairy dust and a prayer but with grit, grace and a fuck tonne of hard work.

Look, moon.

Some of us *are* going to become astronauts; we will look at this milky thumbprint in the sky and think 'yeah, I could totally get there.' And then, if we really want it, we will do the work in order to make that happen — learn how to

199

read the rocket ship instruction manuals in Russian, grow potatoes on Mars, moonwalk… The majority of us however, will never physically get to the moon. Amateur astrologers, our feet will stay planted firmly on the ground as we gaze up in wonder and admiration. The moon will remain for us an aspirational abstract, no more or less beautiful because of it.

A handstand, this pillar of strength and balance, represents something: to some it is a means to confidence, others expression, expansion, creativity, the overcoming of fear. It is elusive, but at the same time tantalisingly close, attainable only for those who are willing to pause their star-gazing, buckle up their spacesuits and commit to a long haul journey of discovery.

Buckle up.

PART V

THE BEGINNINGS

It's all in the mind.

- George Harrison.

Q1: How Do I Start To Handstand?

The Teacher

Please don't demand that your yoga teacher teach you how to handstand. Yoga is a vast and endlessly deep discipline, with branches in philosophy, history and bodywork; you might be lucky enough to have a teacher who has chosen to approach yoga as a broader way of life, if this is the case cherish them, go to their classes often and beg that they never leave the profession. Some teachers relish the prospect of being asked to invert themselves on cue in which case they will run workshops and classes around this theme. There are alternatively some schools such as Rocket, Power Yoga, Dynamic Vinyasa Flow and Tripsichore where handstands are typically part of the sequence taught in class — if this is your jam, seek these out.

The exercises in this book are mostly circus-based. We are lucky enough in Bristol to have a number of highly trained acrobats offering tuition, there are many schools in London most notably the National Centre for Circus Arts and the School of Hand Balancing and Acrobatics run by Sainaa of the Sainaa 4 exercise fame. Wherever you are, your best bet for safe and effective handstand instruction is to seek out a circus hub and ask those who train there who best to go to for tuition. If you can afford it, a one-to-one or small group setting is ideal.

The Equipment

I am thoroughly attached to my yoga mat, it is squidgy
enough to be comfortable and sticky enough for me not to
slide off in sweatier classes. I treasure it as a Barbie-pink
prized possession and for the amount of pennies I shelled
out for it, I better. Some of the exercises that involve being
on our knees can be made kinder on the body by doing
them on a slightly padded surface. This does not have to
be a yoga mat, but it could be. The handstanding itself is
best done on a hard floor; a padded surface offers too
much movement that you have to counterbalance. There is
also a risk of overflexion of the wrists that over time will
definitely hurt. Gabby is not attached to her yoga mat, well
Gabby does not actually own a yoga mat and this is why.
Realistically, all you need for handstanding is:

1) You
2) A Wall
3) A pair of socks
4) A friend to spot and cheer you on
5) … And maybe (boobs dependent) a decent sports bra

The Time/Space Continuum

There are of course, ideal conditions for doing your
handstand practice: a shiny empty studio, all of your props
at your fingertips, a good two hours free and you feeling at
your most fabulous and ready to rock it out. Shockingly,
this mystical alignment does not happen often — more
likely you will have half an hour in your living room,
dressed in pants/pyjamas in that golden gap between
dropping off the kids at school and your next staff meeting

(some extra clothes get thrown on somewhere in there too). And that is also enough. This is what this manual is designed for, for us muggles as well as for acrobats, to use the time that we have to effectively achieve our goals — whatever they may be.

At the beginning of last year, the idea of two self-employed teachers finding the time to write a manual was, quite frankly, laughable. Then we realised how insanely awesome this idea was and we made the time: we set a goal, understood the steps to reach it, gave it a realistic time frame, fed it chocolate and voila! Magic.

As a teacher one of the most common things I hear is "I don't have time." The thing is, finding time for a practice that brings you joy (and perhaps even takes you towards a goal) is important. Whatever that practice is: running, meditation, cycling, yoga, taking extra long bubble baths; people will thank you for it — your partner, your friends, your kids. You will become nicer to be around.

'Finding time' conjures the idea that we are hunting the undiscoverable: precious nuggets of time buried deep within our day... don't give up, they are there.

Q2: How Do I Find The Time?

The best advice I was ever given on how to carve a space out for my practice was 'to write it down in the diary' as if it was a meeting, yes, write it down: 3.45pm 'Meeting (with me)'. That's now your time, right there, written down — a golden nugget to do with as you will and if anybody tries to organise anything in that space you are 'busy'.

After about 20 feet worth of texting, Gabby and I settled on Tuesdays as 'HandstandYogi Day'. HandstandYogi Day has come in many forms and in many venues — in cafes, on trains, one deliciously decadent afternoon spent in a spa but mostly in either of our respective kitchens in our slippers fuelled by Earl Grey tea and Galaxy bars. Behold the glamour.

Q3: How Do I Find The Space?

It is a rare and beautiful thing to have a special place to train. Some use yoga shalas, others dance studios or circus spaces; some our gardens, kitchens or dorm rooms. I am lucky enough to have a space at home to practise.

My Pre-Yoga Rituals:

- Light a candle
- Burn some incense
- Unroll my mat
- Take 3 deep breaths — inhale through the nose and exhale through the mouth

Gabby's Pre-Training Rituals:

- Eat a Jaffa cake

Whatever works.

The Mindset

When I was teaching at a school in North Bristol, every new teacher would get a copy of Carol Dweck's *Mindset* in their pigeon hole at the beginning of the year. Dweck is a professor of Psychology at Stanford University. Having studied the behavioural patterns of thousands of students she coined the terms 'growth' and 'fixed' mindset. Dweck theorises that a fixed mindset values natural talent over hard work. According to Dweck, those with a fixed mindset will tend to shy away from challenges that they can't complete straight away, ignoring constructive feedback and feeling threatened by the success of others. If you would like to see an example of a fixed mindset please see the prologue or in fact any point in this book where I mention my relationship with being upside down. Those of us with a fixed mindset get stuck on the challenge and find it much harder to progress.

A growth mindset on the other hand will relish not being able to accomplish something straight away, using the challenge to fuel their success. They get fierce, and they get better.

This growth and fixed mindset manifests in so many different ways in different aspects of our lives, and is not always so black and white. For example, you might have a growth mindset about handstands because you are naturally athletic and body aware; you might however look at an accounting spreadsheet and run, roadrunner like, through a wall thinking there is no way in hell you'd be able to deal with that. It might be the other way round, just know that you can change your mindset — it just takes practice and the flexing of a whole different set of muscles.

Whatever our mindset, we all have our inner goblins telling us that "you can't do this" or "it's not worth it." Gabby and I have collated our 'Top Five Handstanding Worries' (and tips on how to overcome them): these are your tools to combat those pesky handstand worry goblins.

1) I will fall down
2) I will hurt my wrists
3) I will never be able to do this
4) I am not strong enough
5) I am too heavy to handstand
6) Bonus: I will look ridiculous if I even try

Q4: How Do I Combat The Handstand Worry Goblins? by Gabrielle Parker

1) I will fall down.

The fear of falling over the top is completely understandable. Truth is, you may fall down. There are particular ways you can learn to fall but I would say around 80% of people will naturally fall out the correct way in handstand without even realising they're doing it. Trust your body, body awareness is a wonderful thing that with the right training becomes subconscious. You will be falling like an acrobat in no time.

The Head Stuff

If I don't accept that I may fall down, I will never learn how to fall or how to handstand. I may fall down but I am close to the floor.

The Body Stuff

Option 1 — Find a friend to spot you. Muscle memory is your best friend (after your spotter) in handstand. After multiple repetitions of learning to kick your hips over your shoulders with your friend spotting you, I promise that one day they will move away and you will be doing exactly the same thing.

Option 2 — The wall is a fantastic tool but it soon becomes a crutch that we can never move away from. If you are using the wall, you want to build confidence and endurance in the 'correct form', so rather than kicking up butt to wall consider walking up the wall so your belly is facing it. No part of your body apart from your toes should be resting on the wall. This exercise is one of the best for building up mental and physical confidence in handstand.

Option 3 — Preparing the fall out of handstand.

The most common exit is the side exit, a kind of half cartwheel. If you can't cartwheel, start with a bunny hop travelling sequence (p66) across the room to build the movement pattern in your body. If you can't take any weight on the hands in this half hips over the shoulders position, I'd say realistically that you are not ready to attempt a full handstand yet and instead I would suggest starting with all our basic specific strength building exercises first.

If you are confident with cartwheeling you are ready to put it all together: kick up to handstand, let your hips drift over too far then be decisive and choose one leg, aim your leg towards the floor and your body will follow.

Be Decisive

It's hard not to panic when it is your first few times upside down, I see all sorts of funny flails and little sheep yelps. I think a big part of eliminating this panic, (apart from many repetitions, muscle memory and getting used to the sensation of being upside down on your hands) is being decisive. I had a student the other day in class who clearly wanted to come down from the wall but instead of choosing to come down (in any way he wanted) he flailed against the wall. I said to him across the room, "Dan if you want to come down, be decisive and come down." What did he do? He chose a leg and put it down towards the floor. It sounds very obvious but it's so hard to think logically when you're upside down. Learning to be decisive will not only keep you feeling safe but also it will encourage control, the lack of which is the part that makes most people (and the teacher!) nervous.

2) I will injure my wrists.

Let's face it, handstands are not a natural thing for our bodies to be doing. How do we manage all of that weight on these teeny tiny little wrists? The answer — prehabilitation. Any athlete or artist that specialises in a discipline will specifically condition for their activity. If

211

you want to spend a lot of time on your hands you need to do this too. See wrist strengthening exercises on p119.

If you're training a lot, make sure you have a fabulous sports therapist to support you. Everyone's bodies are different, the way to keep yourself ahead of your injuries is that if you have niggles, manage them properly. Listening to your body is all part of the process.

I can not emphasise enough how important it is to find a good teacher. There are many examples of things that you or your training buddy might not be able to see that could be causing you some wrist discomfort (e.g. you may be balancing the handstand wrong or if you're not accessing enough external rotation). Find a good coach and they will be able to see these things, isolate them and condition them with you.

3) I will never be able to do this.

The short answer to this is that you will be able to do it. I believe that this skill is accessible for almost everyone. Naturally this is dependant on you. If you are dedicated to learning the skill and putting in the graft, you will get it. If you expect to come to four classes and hold a handstand, forget it.

The hardest thing to shift when I coach is mindset. Everyone can do the body stuff — most people better than they realise.

Likewise for me, I could never be a handbalancer or study handbalance. I just don't have the patience for it. After 20 minutes I'm bored, which is why I don't have a one-arm handstand. Sainaa always says to me, when I very rarely manage to make it to his class, "Gabby you could be good but you are laaaazy." I also went to study with Alexander 'Sasha' Gavrilov (one-arm and general handstand guru); he said to me that if I spent three to six months with him I would do a one-armed handstand. I walked out feeling so inspired, but did I do it? No, right now I don't have the right mindset. It's something I'm working on too.

4) *I am not strong enough to handstand.*

Whenever I hear someone tell me that 'I'm not strong enough', I always reply with 'not yet'. You may be very strong in other ways but handstanding requires a specific set of skills. This means you will have to acquire the specific strength that is relevant to this particular skill.

Someone who is strong in running will usually not be strong in netball. People often say to me "oh you're so strong you'll be great at…" People who say this have clearly not seen me try to squat. My personal trainer will gladly tell you that I am a laughable mess when it comes to other skills or exercises.

So in answer to this point: you are strong enough, even if you are not strong enough for this skill… yet.

5) *I am too heavy to handstand.*

The thing is no one is too heavy, too short, too tall. Toby Wells came to me thinking he couldn't handstand at 6'8". "Bullshit," I said, "I'll have great fun spotting you at 4'11"," (it is a comical image, trust me). Yes he's correct in that his body is not naturally designed for this specialisation so I imagine he won't become a professional handbalancer, yet again I'm pretty sure this isn't his objective. Doing a handstand well and being a handbalancer are completely different things. In the same way that at 4'11" I'm not planning on training for the basketball championships, though that doesn't mean I can't play the game.

In circus terms, my body is actually perfectly designed for tumbling but can I tumble? I'm terrified of tumbling, my acro partner used to say to me, "what a waste of a perfect tumbling body Gabby." I'd cry for a good 20 minutes before I'd go for a roundoff flick. Some people's bodies are more naturally designed for particular skills but that doesn't dictate what you want and can do.

6) *I will look ridiculous if I even try.*

Point 1) Many people look ridiculous in the air... There will be a time (if you work hard enough) when you will look like a magical dancing unicorn upside down. Until then, an inverted flailing mess is a completely acceptable alternative.

Point 2) If you embrace looking like a tit, you will progress faster and the journey will be so much more enjoyable. The hard truth is handstanding is not a valuable skill for society, we are not saving the world. Also, handstands aren't vegetables — you aren't going to become a healthier person by doing more of them. You might as a byproduct but handstands themselves are not innately good for you.

The main benefits of handstands? Looking cool and battling your own personal demons that say you can not do this. You can do this. Try to remove some of the pressure and enjoy the struggle.

Magic (n) The power of apparently influencing events by using mysterious or supernatural forces.
Example 'suddenly, as if by magic, the doors start to open.'

— Oxford English Dictionary

Epilogue

BRISTOL, MAY 2017

Two years later and I was back on *that* wall. It was not easier, in fact having done little or no actual handstand training (and an awful lot more computer work) in those 24 months, it was most definitely harder.

In the next minute upside down there followed a series of revelations:

18:15:05. Ok. Breathe. Remember you wrote that chapter on how important breathing is? Remember? Long inhale, loong exhale. Long inhale…

18:15:25. Forget the breath, this is about survival.

18:15:35. I am never ever *ever* handstanding ever *ever* again.

18:15:45. Maybe I'll quit yoga and take up something more soothing like DJing, vampire slaying or krav maga…

18:15:50. Thank god I bought that new sports bra.

18:16:00. Ah, I'm down. OK, that wasn't so bad. I love Gabby, she is such a great teacher.

18:18:00. Seriously, she wants me to go upside down *again*? I do NOT love Gabby.

…

Simon, the illustrator of this book and Gabby's partner, is also a magician. A real one with card tricks, stuff up (and tattooed upon) his sleeves and a referral from Derren Brown. Wizard though he is, Simon is especially fond of the phrase 'there is no hocus pocus'. This is a quote from SW Erdnase, the early 20th century author of *The Expert at the Card Table*. This book reveals the sleight of hand and sneaky cheat techniques used by card playing professionals and has not gone out of print in over 100 years.

Find yourself in any London-based dynamic yoga class and you will likely find yourself in the presence of one of these 'expert[s] at the table'. An inversion variation being offered, these handstand athletes will lift themselves upside down with grace, ease and beauty as if they popped out of the womb in a perfect press.

They (I am 98% sure) did not.

Though it would make the marketing for this particular book a lot easier, the thing is there *is* no 'hocus pocus' when it comes to handstands — no dust made from ground-up unicorn horn to mix with your matcha latte (though, if effective, would probably be both disgusting, very expensive and sold in every studio), no 30-day plan, no leggings to lift your butt so high it floats off the floor. Believe me, I've looked.

It may not be 'hocus pocus', but it is also not rocket science. Beyond the rippling abdominals, toned shoulders and swishy ponytails that so often come with the handstand package, lies the hard grind, sweat, and intelligent training. When praising this beautiful pose we are also applauding all of the mornings when those practitioners hauled themselves out of bed, denying themselves that extra morning snuggle time and the chance to do the crossword, or drove themselves to an awkwardly-scheduled evening class instead of to the pub. In looking at that inspirational Instagram feed we are also gazing dumbstruck at those hours that they have spent practising to make something so incredibly difficult look so enviably effortless.

All of those hours of practice that given my current gelatinous handstanding form, I clearly have not done. Yet.

Back in class, I sloshed over to Gabby at the end of session. My muscles were buzzing: triceps, biceps, back and butt. I felt alive, unusually pumped up with endorphin-dosed zeal. It was time to assert my mission.

"Gabbs, I think I'd like to learn to handstand. You know, properly."

She looked up from stuffing resistance bands into her duffel bag.

"Why?"

"Why? Because they are SEXY, Gabby. *Obviously.*"

Gabby nodded silently and started to pull on her old jogging bottoms over her leggings, her iPhone gripped vice-like between her teeth. Her foot got caught in the trouser leg and she hopped about a bit until she wobbled back into balance.

Yep, really, *really* sexy.

The Players

The Handstander: Gabrielle Parker
bristolhandstands.com

The Yogi: Ash Bond
flyingmonkeyyoga.org

The Illustrator: SimonSi
@simonsi

To all the handstanding yogis below and more, thank you for your time, energy and the willingness to be emailed at one in the morning with questions that just got more and more geeky. You are all magic.

The Rockstar Yogi: Les Leventhal
yogawithles.com

The Wizard Yogi: Jambo Truong
jambodragonyoga.com

The Yogi Like Water: Dan Peppiatt
yogalikewater.com

The Super Yogi: Will Dukes
superyogi.co.uk

The Power Yogi: Denise Payne
denisepayneyoga.com

The Wonder Yogi: Ambra Vallo
ambrasana.com

The Batman Yogi: Reuben Hosler
reubenhoslerseo.ca

The Yin Yang Yogi: Matt Pasquet
mattpasquet.com

Thank you to our wonderful models Matt, Isaac, Jason, Imogen, Rachel and Will for their endless handstanding skill and patience.

To our many teachers whose words and exercises we have shamelessly mined to enrich this book, thank you for offering them freely and without any legal complications.

Special thanks to Sarah Perry *(yogafunction.com)*, Janchivdorj Sainbayar *(@london_school_of_hand_balance_)* and Nicolas Montes De Oca *(@nicolastanding)*.

Thank you also to the yogis at *Soul Circus Yoga Festival* for believing in us when *The Handstanding Yogi* was nothing more than a catchy title and a pile of scribbled notebooks. Thank you for allowing us to launch our dream on your stage. *www.soulcircus.yoga*

The Books

On the History of Yoga

Singleton, M. (2010). *Yoga Body*. Oxford: Oxford University Press.
Broad, W. (2013). The Science of Yoga. New York. Simon & Schuster.

On Breath

Iyengar, B. (1981). *Light on Pranayama*. London: Harper Thorsons.

On Yoga Posture

Iyengar, B. (1976). *Light on Yoga*. London: Thorsons.

On Rocket Yoga

YouTube. (2017). *In loving memory of Larry Schultz-Rocket Man*. [online] Available at: https://www.youtube.com/watch?v=fHPJ_lyRWcQ

On Restorative Yoga

Carey, L. (2013). *The Yapana Way*. Redondo Beach, CA. Leeann Carey Yoga.
Lasater, J. (2011). *Relax and Renew*. Berkeley, CA: Rodmell Press.

On Ashtanga Yoga

Jois, K. (2013). *Yoga Mala*. New York: Farrar, Straus and Giroux.
Scott, J. (2000). *Ashtanga Yoga*. New York: Three Rivers Press.

On Mindset

Dweck, C. (2006). *Mindset: The New Psychology of Success.* New York: Random House

On Our Favourite Yogis

Leventhal, L. and Levasseur, B. (2014). *Two Lifestyles, One Lifetime.*

Budig, K. (2016). *Aim True*. New York: William Morrow.

Notes

Notes

How is it going?

Follow our handstand journey and share your stories on
handstandyogi.com/category/handstand-diaries/

⊙ @handstandyogi

ⓕ HandstandYogi

✉ hello@handstandyogi.com